...terpreted by Geology.

FEATURES ...ctive layers	CHIEF FEATURES OF PERIODS IN THEIR ORDER ↓	GENESIS 1 verses 1 to 26 (read from bottom upwards)
	MAN WITH DOMINION	**6th DAY** — GOD SAID — Let us make MAN in our image. Let them have dominion over the FISH, ..FOWL..CATTLE and CREEPING THINGS (v.26)
	CATTLE AND WILD **BEASTS**	GOD SAID — Let the Earth bring forth the living creature, AFTER HIS KIND and CATTLE, AFTER THEIR KIND and creeping thing and beast of the Earth AFTER THEIR KIND. (v.24)
	GREAT **MONSTERS REPTILES** AND **FLYING THINGS**	**5th DAY** — GOD created GREAT MONSTERS. GOD SAID — Let the waters swarm with swarms of the living creature that moveth AFTER HIS KIND. (v.21) Let WINGED THINGS fly. (v.20)
...e dies out. ...s in Australia 10b ...thern Hem. ...s in Europe.	**SEASONS YEARS & DAYS**	**4th DAY** — GOD SAID — Let lights in the Expanse divide the Day from the Night and let them be for signs and for seasons and for days and for years. (v.14,15,16.)
...ons ...id down	**VEGETATION** PLANTS & TREES WITH SEEDS	**3rd DAY** — GOD SAID — Let the Earth bring forth tender sproutage and herb yielding seed AFTER HIS KIND and fruit tree yielding fruit whose seed is in itself (v.11)(v.12)
6b 7 ...rial life 7	**DRY LAND**	GOD SAID — Let the dry land appear. (v.9)
...) 4	**EXPANSE** OR **ATMOSPHERE**	**2nd DAY** — GOD SAID — Let there be an expanse in the midst of the waters. Let it divide the waters (CLOUDS) from the waters (OCEAN).
...CK Lower Cambrian	**LIGHT**	GOD SAID — Let there be light. (v.3)
(Algae) 4 5	**CREATION OF MARINE LIFE**	**1st DAY** — THE SPIRIT OF GOD WAS CONTINUALLY BROODING OVER THE FACE OF THE WATERS. (v.2)
KNOWN		
...ng the Earth 3	**DARKNESS UPON THE OCEAN**	DARKNESS WAS UPON THE FACE OF THE [ROARING] DEEP.
...16 in ...hand columns	**OCEAN BORN EARTH UNFORMED** **CREATION**	(read Job 38 verses 4–11) THE EARTH WAS UNFORMED AND EMPTY (v.2.) IN THE BEGINNING GOD CREATED THE HEAVENS AND THE EARTH. (v.1)

...GY. 174 Collins St., Melbourne.

READ UPWARDS

CREATION'S
AMAZING
ARCHITECT

CREATION'S AMAZING ARCHITECT

Walter J. Beasley, F.R.G.S.

PRESIDENT OF THE
AUSTRALIAN INSTITUTE OF ARCHAEOLOGY
COLLINS STREET, MELBOURNE

AUTHOR OF
"JERICHO'S JUDGMENT"

Illustrations by
A. V. BROWN

London
MARSHALL, MORGAN & SCOTT
Edinburgh

LONDON
MARSHALL, MORGAN AND SCOTT, LTD.
1–5 PORTPOOL LANE
HOLBORN, E.C.1

CANADA
EVANGELICAL PUBLISHERS
241 YONGE STREET
TORONTO

AUSTRALIA
119 BURWOOD ROAD
MELBOURNE, E.13

SOUTH AFRICA
P.O. BOX 1720, STURK'S BUILDINGS
CAPE TOWN

U.S.A.
ZONDERVAN PUBLISHING HOUSE
1415 LAKE DRIVE, S.E.
GRAND RAPIDS 6, MICHIGAN

MADE AND PRINTED IN GREAT BRITAIN BY PURNELL AND SONS, LTD,
PAULTON (SOMERSET) AND LONDON

Mr. Walter J. Beasley has undertaken a very grateful but difficult task of reconciling the Creation report of the first chapter of Genesis with the theories about the origin of the universe arrived at by modern geology.

In support of the veracity of the O.T. cosmogony Mr. Beasley quoted extracts from Job, Isaiah and Proverbs.

The translations of the Hebrew passages quoted in his book are accurate and hold their own without doing injustice to the Hebrew original, even where the translation chosen by him diverges from the versions of commonly known translations. His interpretation of individual words and phrases, which serve to support his theory, is consistent with the spirit of the Hebrew language.

M. D. GOLDMAN

Professor of Semitic Studies,
The University of Melbourne.

This book is dedicated
to devoted research workers
who search after Truth—
the whole Truth
and nothing but the Truth

CONTENTS

		Page
PROLOGUE		17
THE ETERNAL WISDOM . . .		21

Chapter

I. THE FIRST ERA:
   THE ORIGIN OF THE UNIVERSE . 27

   The Eternal Architect plans—An exhibition of Infinite
   Wisdom—The realms of space—Galaxies by the million
   —A dwelling site for man—Ancient wisdom contrasted—
   The dwelling site, its early chaotic condition—Its bar-
   renness—When cooling started.

II. THE FIRST ERA (*continued*):
    THE FOUNDATIONS OF THE EARTH . 39

    The Foundations For The Home : The dense central core
    —The immense weight of the ocean—The predeter-
    mined measurements of the home—The earth's size
    determined its atmosphere—The influence of space
    neighbours—If—A moon the size of the earth—The
    deep foundations—The foundations of our continent—
    The immense cornerstone.
    The Ocean : Its birthplace—Its mysterious beginning—
    Its early clothing—Its early domination.

III. THE FIRST ERA (*continued*):
     LET THERE BE LIGHT 57

     The Ocean : Its chaotic condition—Geology reveals
     creative processes—The dark and turbulent ocean—The
     majestic lighting systems—Automatic controls.
     The First Life : Certain early life was specialised—
     World-wide search for precursors—The first life was
     diversified—Where did life come from?—The Spirit of
     God the source of all life—The continuity of brooding
     upon the waters—The pastures of the sea—Single-celled
     life is complex—The wonders of amoeba—Life in a
     coral pool—Plants and animals need each other—Food
     delivered by sunlight.

Chapter *Page*

IV. THE SECOND ERA:
THE ESTABLISHMENT OF THE ATMOS-
PHERE 73

The Vital Air-conditioning System : The atmosphere is
spread as a tent—The early adjustment of the atmosphere
—Atmospheric water storage—The exquisite planning of
the Architect.

V. THE THIRD ERA:
DRY LAND AND VEGETATION APPEAR 81

How Dry Land Formed : The soil for the home garden—
The sea floor lifted, the sea retreated—The first plants
arrive—An Architect who delighted in creating—
Mechanical reproduction in the garden—Magical multi-
plication—The difficulties of early seaweeds—Drought-
resisting seaweeds?—The coal supply for the home—
Luxuriant forests produced coal—The magnificent
manufacturer—World-wide deposits.

VI. THE FOURTH ERA:
THE CLEARING OF THE ATMOSPHERE 95

Lights Appointed To Dominate : The lighting system of
the home modernised—The Hebrew exactness—Drastic
changes noted—The universal calendar—The moon
appointed for seasons—Palaeozoic Era closes with
climatic changes—Summary.

VII. THE FIFTH ERA:
GREAT MONSTERS AND MODERN
PLANTS 106

Great Monsters Have Their Day : New occupants in
possession of the grounds—Swiftly gliding sea-monsters
—Flying things are introduced—Science anticipated by
Scripture—The creation of modern plants and grasses—
Sudden invasion by modern plants—Fossil facts are
stubborn things—Food arrives before animals—Modern
flowers need sunlight—Sudden arrivals change a theory.

VIII. THE SIXTH ERA:
LAND MAMMALS 121

The provision for domestic supplies—The miracle of
reproduction—The miracle of the pollen—Like father
like son—Where are the missing links?
Days Can Be Eras : Scientific details anticipated in
Genesis—The use of YOM in Genesis—The Day in the
wilderness—" Yom " used for a period—Fossils reveal

Chapter *Page*

normal development—The evidence of the coal beds—The evidence of the monsters.
Evening and Morning : Planning and accomplishment— The amazing Architect planned creation—God saw that it was very good.

IX. THE SIXTH ERA (*continued*):
MAN, GOD'S LIVING MASTERPIECE . 135

Man Alone Exploits The Earth : The earth made for man —Confusion about early man—The earliest village life in Asia—The problem of Glacial periods—The problem of Palaeolithic man—The Scripture presentation— Reconstructed theories about early man—Fossil apes disprove a theory—Archaeological evidence about a flood.

EPILOGUE 143

Chance evolution or a predetermined creation—Sacred writers repudiate chance—Purposeful creation—All life reproduces after its kind—An orderly complicated creation cannot come by chance—Reproduction of living things a complicated process—A complicated process demands superior intelligence.

THE ETERNAL MAJESTY 149

BIBLICAL ORDER OF CREATION and the order suggested by scientists—Forty-six facts correlated 151

APPENDIX A 155

TABLES OF GEOLOGICAL PERIODS AND EVENTS

Compared with the Scripture Statements

TABLE A. *GEOLOGICAL PERIODS:*
The scientific story of created things . **Page 22**

TABLE B. *EVENTS OF THE FIRST "DAY" (BEFORE AND DURING THE PRECAMBRIAN ERA).*
From the earth's formless condition to the coming of light and life 38

TABLE C. *EVENTS OF THE SECOND AND THIRD "DAYS" (FROM THE PRECAMBRIAN ERA TO THE PERMIAN PERIOD).*
Adjustment of the atmosphere. The continuous creation of marine life. The creation of land vegetation 80

TABLE D. *EVENTS OF THE FOURTH "DAY" (FROM THE PERMIAN PERIOD TO THE MESOZOIC ERA).*
Great climatic changes—the domination of the sun and moon in the atmosphere. Permanent seasonal conditions . . . 94

TABLE E. *EVENTS OF THE FIFTH "DAY" (THE MESOZOIC ERA).*
The creation of great reptilian sea and land monsters. The creation of flying things. Creation of modern flowering plants . . 104

TABLE F. *EVENTS OF THE SIXTH "DAY" (THE CAINOZOIC ERA).*
The creation of beasts of the earth, cattle, etc. (land mammals). The creation of man . 120

Page

TABLE G. *COMPARISON OF THE ORDER OF CREATED THINGS* as outlined by Science and the Bible   151

PROLOGUE

HOW WAS THE WORLD MADE?

Fortunately man as we see him today is incurably inquisitive. It is not sufficient that he has been placed for the most part in very delightful physical surroundings, upon a unique sphere in space, but he must needs know just how that sphere was fashioned and of what materials it has been made. He has an intense desire to understand some of the various processes that the materials passed through before they came to such a condition as he beholds at present.

Two Records of Creation Available

Two records of the processes were available for research to curious minds. One record, and by far the more detailed, remained hidden for centuries, until men began to scientifically investigate the rocks and their materials, and the layers of the earth and their fossils. This involved patient investigations which extended over many lands during the past 150 years, and engaged the attention of thousands of students of geology, botany and palaeontology.

In various layers of the crust were discovered the fossilised remains of the early life that was introduced into the world and placed within its waters. Little by little the fascinating jig-saw puzzle of the various periods was placed together, until at last there emerged a more or less complete picture of the diversified types of vegetable and animal life that lived upon the earth in distant ages. This record of the rocks and the fossil evidence they contained was the result of very patient investigation that sometimes entailed much personal sacrifice on the part of many of its students.

The Second Record

There is a second record—the Bible—available to men. It is by no means as detailed in its scientific presentation as the one investigated by the geologists, but nevertheless it is a very valuable one. If the Sacred Record can be shown to be in harmony with the independently ascertained facts of modern scientific research, then surely such an anticipation by about 3,500 years must constitute a tremendous challenge to the people of this scientific age. Again, when we correlate these two records, surely it demonstrates that the Author of the sacred record is the Author of the rocks and their fossil evidence.

Now the Hebrew Scriptures have come down to us through the centuries. These records profess to be divinely revealed and authorised (Gen. 1: 1; Exod. 4: 11–12; 8: 1; 20: 1; 24: 3–4; Deut. 34: 10). One way by which we can test such claims is to place the two records alongside each other. This is the intention of the book. The scripture portions have been presented as accurately as the available Hebrew documents will allow, and the available scientific material has been used as a commentary.

In the past the usual practice has been to place the Hebrew text alongside myths and traditions that have come to us from Babylonian, Assyrian, Sumerian and other sources. The more light that comes to us from these quarters, however, the more the evidence seems to suggest a manipulation of a yet earlier primeval revelation. The personification of the elements of nature in certain of these accounts seems to suggest that the confusion now observed was by no means accidental.

Confusion Caused by Theories

It must be remembered that in recent years there has been a great deal of confusion in both theological and scientific circles, caused largely on the one hand by the factual material of the scientists, being interpreted by certain theories that had by no means been proved. Many Bible students turned away completely from such interpretations, but in doing so missed many very interesting facts relative to the creative processes made available by geologists and palaeontologists.

On the other hand, many scientific men turned aside from the Biblical viewpoint as expressed in the Authorised Version of the first chapter of Genesis and the Book of Job, because, as we shall see later, the English translations used did not do justice to the language in which the stories were written, and in the second place because a new theory introduced by theologians interpreted these narratives by the aid of Babylonian stories of creation as discovered in the palace library of Ashur-bani-pal at Nineveh and elsewhere.

REPRESENTATIVE AUTHORITIES USED

It may be thought by some readers that the writer has been tempted to select only the authorities that agree with his interpretation, but it will be seen that this viewpoint has been anticipated by selecting those who are the representative authorities in their branch of research. Other readers may think that the evidence opposed to the theory of chance evolution has been overstressed. It must be kept in mind that these pages have not been written for scientific men but for the average person who has never had an opportunity of doing any research either secular or sacred. All readers of the scriptures are entitled to know that there is another interpretation of the available scientific material that does not destroy their faith in its accuracy or inspiration. For years people have read books whose authors have openly accepted the theory of chance evolution as though it had been an established scientific fact, and many of these writers have just as openly ridiculed the Bible account (Authorised Version) without considering the fact that this translation was made in 1611, or about 200 years before the investigations of geologists began. If, among other things, the translators of 1611 erred in calling "great monsters" by the name of "whales", such a translation was surely pardonable at the time, because the "great monsters" of the Mesozoic Period of geology were most likely then unknown or, if known, unclassified.

It will be seen from the following pages that neither the student of the various sciences nor the student of the Mosaic documents has any need to be afraid about ultimate truth so long as the facts on both sides are clearly set alongside each other, without using interpretations based upon unproved or confused theories.

To the many friends who have assisted with supplying translations of the Hebrew or reading and supplying helpful criticisms of the manuscript, my sincere thanks are due.

I trust as a result of reading this presentation that many people will take the first opportunity of making themselves more familiar with the scientific evidence available today upon this fascinating subject. Even if books cannot always be purchased because of price or shortage of stocks, some books from lending libraries are usually available. It will always give much personal satisfaction to be able to follow more closely the details of such a tremendous subject as this one introduces to us.

THE ETERNAL WISDOM

"I WISDOM . . .
The Lord possessed me in the beginning of his way,
Before his works of old.
I was set up from everlasting,
From the beginning,
Or ever the earth was.
When there were no depths, I was brought forth;
When there were no fountains abounding with water.
Before the mountains were settled, before the hills was
I brought forth:
While as yet he had not made the earth, nor the fields,
nor the highest part of the dust of the world.
When he prepared the heavens, I was there:
When he set a compass upon the face of the depth:
When he established the clouds above:
When he strengthened the fountains of the deep:
When he gave to the sea his decree, that the waters
should not pass his commandment:
When he appointed the foundations of the earth."

Proverbs 8: 12, 22-9.

TABLE A

THE SCIENTIFIC STORY OF CREATED THINGS

Read from opposite page upwards.

GEOLOGICAL PERIODS		SOME OF THE CHIEF EVENTS OF CREATION CORRELATED WITH THEIR GEOLOGICAL PERIODS	BIBLICAL CORRELATIONS
CAINOZOIC ERA	Holocene		See details on Tables B, C, D, E, F.
	Pleistocene	Man Glacial Periods	{ Man created in God's image (Gen. 1:27)
	Pliocene	Modern mammals	
	Miocene	Cattle, etc.	{ God made beast of the earth, cattle, etc. (Gen. 1:25)
	Oligocene	Early land mammals	
	Eocene		
MESOZOIC ERA	Cretaceous	Modern flowering plants Bees	
	Jurassic	First flying creatures Great reptilian monsters	{ God created great monsters, flying things, etc. (Gen. 1:21)
	Triassic	New life appears Great climatic changes including desert conditions in Europe	{ God appointed two great lights to dominate day and night and seasons (Gen. 1:16)
PALAEOZOIC ERA	Permian	Palaeozoic life dies out Glacial Period	
	Carboniferous	Coal deposits—amphibians Luxuriant vegetation	
	Devonian	Trees in forest, proportions Marine vertebrates arrive Insects	{ Let the earth bring forth tender sproutage, herb yielding seed, tree yielding fruit (Gen. 1:11)
	Silurian	Early land vegetation Land uplift (2)	
	Ordovician	Graptolites Corals	
	Cambrian	Abundant marine life arrives (invertebrates) Trilobites, sponges, shell-fish, jellyfish, starfish, worms No terrestrial life known	{ The Spirit of God brooding continually upon the waters (Gen. 1:2)

Begin from lower part of opposite page, then continue upwards from here.

GEOLOGICAL PERIODS		SOME OF THE CHIEF EVENTS OF CREATION CORRELATED WITH THEIR GEOLOGICAL PERIODS	BIBLICAL CORRELATIONS
PRE-CAMBRIAN ERA	Proterozoic	First seaweeds Worm tracks	{ Let the waters be gathered together and dry land appear (Gen. 1: 9)
	Archaeozoic	Life uncertain Early land uplift (1) Atmosphere established(?) Light comes to the earth	{ Let there be an expanse in the midst of the waters (Gen. 1: 6) Light
Formation of the hot earth-mass		Darkness surrounds the earth-mass Ocean born	{ Spirit of God brooding upon the waters continually (Gen. 1: 2) Ocean born and darkness surrounds it
		Earth-mass cooling Earth without form Creation of the earth begins	{ Foundations (Job 38: 4–11; Gen. 1: 1)

Read upwards ↑   *Read upwards* ↑

23

THE FIRST ERA:
THE ORIGIN OF THE UNIVERSE

(Refer to bottom of Tables A and B)

"In the beginning God created the heaven and the earth. And the earth was without form and void [glowing and empty]."

Genesis 1: 1-2.

THE FIRST ERA:
THE ORIGIN OF THE UNIVERSE

Science is inquisitiveness organised.

"In the beginning"
(Gen. 1: 1).

THE ETERNAL ARCHITECT PLANS

Modern astronomers, geologists and other scientists who seek to probe the problems of the early history of the earth and its life agree that the facts discovered by science point to a period when there was a definite beginning to the earth and other physical things.

At one time certain schools of thought taught that the earth and spheres were eternal.(1)

A most natural question arises: "How far back in the distant ages did God begin His creation?" Here is one measuring instrument, used by scientific men, that may help to enlighten us.

Light travels at about 186,000 miles per second. To reach the earth from the moon, which is our nearest heavenly neighbour, light takes $1\frac{1}{4}$ seconds; from the sun it take 8 minutes. To go outside our planetary system it takes 4 hours. To come from the earth's nearest star-neighbour it would need to travel non-stop for four years. To come from the nebulae of Andromeda it would take 800,000 years.(2)

At Palomar, California, the latest telescope, for instance, has been able to photograph some distant spheres, the light of which would not reach the earth for 2,000 million years.(3) If one of these distant suns were to explode at the moment it was being photographed from the earth, the explosion could not be seen for another 2,000 million years. This parade of facts does not answer our question, but it helps us to understand something of the enormous periods of time that must be wrapped up in the history of creation, when light from these distant spheres takes such a tremendous time to reach us.

Scientists, however, have made certain calculations. Some have estimated the age of the earth at anything from 28 million to over 3,000 million years.(4) The age of the sun has been stated by Sir James Jeans to be about 7 million million years, and even longer periods are given for other stars, while the age of the universe has been estimated up to millions of millions of years.(5) In other words, when men try to measure a fragment of eternity with human measurements they find the process extremely difficult!

As for the creation of the universe or of our planetary system, any number of years demanded by scientists may be allowed for in the phrase used in the scripture presentation:

"In the beginning God created the heaven and the earth."

An Exhibition of Infinite Wisdom

In any great engineering work, such as the Sydney Harbour Bridge, which had to be very carefully planned to take the tremendous strain of its own weight and of many trains, trams, buses, motor-cars and people, as well as the added stress of occasional wind storms, there must have been highly trained and experienced draughtsmen and engineers.

In the erection of any large modern building there must be highly specialised architects and workmen to plan and produce such a structure. Architectural development, from the foundations to the completion of all essential internal details, such as

The more complicated and specialised the structure, the greater is the intelligence needed to plan and complete it.

"God Created" (Gen. 1:1).

water supply, sewerage, ventilation, heating, lighting, telephones, stairways, fire prevention, etc., demands efficient thinking and anticipated planning.

In building a universe there must first be some plan prepared by an All-wise Intelligence—a Builder who can specialise in creating worlds, spheres without number, and all kinds of living things—a Supreme Architect, whose Wisdom is amply demonstrated in the magnificent planning, co-ordination, perfection and beauty of all His works of multitudinous variety.

English-speaking peoples will need to pause just here and ask the question, "What did the ancient scribe understand when he used the Hebrew word 'BARA', which has been translated 'CREATE'?" Various theories have been built upon the idea of God creating something suddenly out of nothing, which would be complete and perfect. It is worthwhile looking into the Biblical usage of the word to discover for ourselves its peculiar value, and to see whether this theory is correct or not, by comparing the usage of the several words employed with other passages in the Scriptures. This has been done, and will be found in Appendix A at the end of the book.

"God created the heaven"
(Gen. 1: 1).

IN THE REALMS OF SPACE

Many theories have been advanced by scientists as to HOW they think THE HEAVENS (containing spheres, suns and systems) progressed from primeval conditions. The Genesis writer did NOT attempt to explain HOW God created things; he merely stated the FACT and set down *the order* in which various things were created.

We have illustrated one theory advanced;(6) but as scientific men have not been able to agree as to HOW the host of THE HEAVENS was created, let us pass on to the FACT itself and see what astronomers say about THE HEAVENS.

WORLDS WITHOUT END

Mr. G. F. Dodwell, Government Astronomer at the Adelaide Observatory, in answering a question put to him by the writer, said:

"Thinking of Eternity as endless time, we similarly think of endless space, and possibly endless worlds, or at least a number so vast that it baffles the imagination."

Dr. Harlow Shappley used other words.(7) He wrote:

"I have estimated from available meta-galactic census that more than 20 million galaxies are within range of our telescopes. Our greatest telescopes do not reach all the way, and a fair estimate would make the total number of galaxies in the universe greater than 1 million million."

GALAXIES BY THE MILLION

He also tells us that one galaxy (such as the great group of stars which makes up our own particular universe) would probably contain about 10 billion stars. Would our estimate of the number of stars be too high, too low, or about right if we multiplied the estimated number of stars said to be contained in the *one galaxy* mentioned (10 billion) by the number of estimated galaxies (1 million million)?

Scientists at the time of Christ estimated the number of stars at about 3,000, which is about the number that can be observed by the naked eye.(8) But centuries before this a more ancient writer declared:

"The host of heaven cannot be numbered, neither the sand of the sea measured" (Jer. 33: 22).

This opinion is nearer to that of modern scientists than was the opinion of scientists at the time of Christ.

> "And the earth" (Gen. 1: 1).

A Dwelling Site for Man

The modern scientist even if he cannot state the precise origin of the earth at least realises that it is part of the universe around it. He realises that, whatever may be the origin of other spheres, the earth had a similar sort of origin. The Genesis writer agrees in this, that the origin of all heavenly bodies is to be found in a creative act of God.

Of known ancient sources the most scientific account of the earth's position in space comes from the Hebrew scriptures.

It is interesting at this point to collect other Bible statements about the earth and compare or contrast these with the ideas of other ancient peoples, and with the statements of modern scientists.

At least 3,000 years ago one Bible writer was able to state the fact:

"He . . . hangeth the earth upon nothing" (Job 26: 7).

Other sacred writers refer to:

"The circle of the earth" (Isa. 40: 22).
"He set a compass [or a circle] upon the face of the deep" (Prov. 8: 27).

Surely there is a peculiar accuracy and uniqueness about these Bible statements that certainly does not conflict with modern science.

ANCIENT WISDOM CONTRASTED

By contrast the sages of India taught that the earth was supported on the backs of elephants who stood upon a tortoise which swam in the waters. The Greeks, renowned for their wisdom, taught that the world was supported on the back of Atlas. The Babylonians taught that the earth was flat. This view is still held by Arabs today, who tell the story of unbelievers being pushed over the sides into space.

A few facts about our earth and the other members of the family of planets may be of interest. These facts will increase our wonder and reverence for the mighty thing that God has done. Our earth is said to contain about 267,000 million cubic miles and have a mass of about 5,000 million million million tons.(9) But we are informed that the planet SATURN could take into its body 900 spheres the size of the earth. The planet JUPITER, however, could accommodate 1,300 earth-spheres, while the SUN would take 1,300,000 of them. However, lest we be taken up too much with family affairs, we are told that the nebulae of Andromeda, 800,000 light years away, could compass 1 million million million million million *suns*.(10)

With regard to the distances between the sun and its family

of planets, an interesting comparison has been given to us by a recent writer: **(10A)**

"Suppose we make a plan of how the sun and the planets are arranged. In our plan, let us represent the sun as a ball, six inches in diameter, the sort of thing you could easily hold in one hand. This, by the way, is a reduction in a scale of nearly 10,000,000,000. Now, how far away are our planets from our ball? Not a few feet or one or two yards, as many people imagine in their subconscious picture of the solar system, but very much more. Mercury is 7 yards away, Venus about 13 yards, the Earth 18 yards, Mars 27 yards, Jupiter 90 yards, Saturn 170 yards, and Pluto 710 yards. On this scale, the Earth is represented as a speck of dust, and the nearest stars are about 2,000 miles away."

> **"And the earth was without form"** (Gen. 1: 2).

THE DWELLING SITE—ITS EARLY CHAOTIC CONDITION

Sir James Jeans and others have given us theories as to how they think the earth came into being.**(11)** The following processes have been suggested:

1. The earth was at first a gas (as it perhaps came out of a sun).
2. It then became a liquid at a very high temperature.
3. Later, as it lost heat, it became a hot plastic mass.
4. It cooled with a solid crust as at present.

Some scientists do not agree about the details of the process contained in the theory that uses items Nos. 1 and 2.**(12)** However, most agree that eventually the outer portion of the earth became a hot plastic mass (No. 3), which afterwards cooled to its present stage (No. 4).

WHEN COOLING STARTED

One writer has supplied us with some data dealing with this period. He has told us that a very interesting series of events would take place once cooling started.**(13)** At about 7,000°F. the first chemical compounds would be formed. Then, when the temperature dropped to about 4,500°F., the oxygen would combine with a host of materials, and the very foundations of the earth would be laid, although at the surface it would be something like a boiling cauldron. When the temperature fell to about

Illustration of one scientific theory which suggests the beginning of the planetary system.

3,400°F., the crust, formed mainly of silicate rocks, would consolidate.

The important thing for us to notice, however, is that the sacred writer anticipated by about 3,500 years the modern scientist on these details regarding the early condition of the earth-mass. With a minimum of words, but with great depth of meaning, he described man's future home as being unformed and unfurnished. As we proceed we shall notice that the Bible narratives describe the structural necessities for the house, then the order in which the furnishings were introduced, and, later, details of the life which occupied it. We shall not only observe that the order in which all these were introduced is scientifically correct, but we shall see that there are groups of things mentioned together, and these display a remarkably intimate anticipation of events which are in perfect harmony with modern scientific investigation. Surely no other book on earth has anticipated such knowledge!

> **"And void [of life]" (Gen. 1: 2).**

THE DWELLING SITE—ITS BARRENNESS

As one reads further in this first chapter of Genesis it becomes evident that the writer is describing the various steps in which God prepared the earth for life, and the order in which He created life upon it. It is the story of how life came.

Now the Hebrew phrasing here conveys the idea of emptiness. Various attempts have been made to translate two Hebrew words —"Without form and void" (Authorised Version), "an empty waste" (Knox), "unformed and void" (Jewish translation), "void and empty" (Douay).

Professor M. D. Goldman, of the School of Semitic Studies in the University of Melbourne, has informed us that a study of cognate words in Arabic the phrase could be translated "Brightness and Desert" which is a figure of speech of some such idea as "A bright waste" or "Glowing emptiness". The sacred writer would seem to be presenting us with a picture of the time when, according to the modern scientists, the earth was an empty glowing waste and certainly with no form of life.

Illustration of another theory which suggests that the solid earth began as a gas.

BIBLIOGRAPHY

1. *The Origin of the Earth*, pp. 101, 103, W. M. Smart, 1950. **2.** *The World, Whence and How* (Enc. of Modern Knowledge), p. 14, Sir J. Jeans. **3.** *National Geographic Magazine* p. 402, vol. XCVIII, No. 3, Sept. 1950. **4.** *The Succession of Life Through Geological Time*, p. 63, British Museum (Natural History), 1949. **5.** Ref. as (2), p. 143. **6.** Ref. as (2), p. 135. **7.** *American Journal of Science*, pp. 508–22, vol. 243 A. **8.** *The Outline of the Universe*, p. 47, J. G. Crowther, 1938. **9.** Ref. as (1), p. 27. **10.** Ref. as (2), pp. 143–4, vol. 1. **10A** *The Nature of the Universe*, p. 15, F. Hoyle. **11.** Ref. as (2), p. 4. **12.** *The World in the Past*, pp. 44–5, B. Webster Smith, 1945. **13.** *The Corridor of Life*, p. 25, Swinton and Pinner, 1948.

CHAPTER II

THE FIRST ERA (*continued*):
THE FOUNDATIONS OF THE EARTH

The Sacred Records: Job 38: 4–11

"The Lord . . . said:
Where wast thou when I laid the foundations of the earth?
  declare if thou hast understanding.
Who determined the measures thereof, if thou knowest?
  or who hath stretched the line upon it?
Whereupon are the foundations thereof fastened?
  or who laid the cornerstone thereof?
Or who shut up the sea with doors, when it brake forth,
  as it issued out of the womb?
When I made the cloud the garment thereof, and thick
  darkness a swaddling-band for it.
And established my decree upon it, and set bars and doors,
And said, Hitherto shalt thou come, but no further:
And here shall the pride of thy waves be stayed?"

Job 38: 4–11.

CORRELATION OF GEOLOGICAL MATERIAL WITH THE SCRIPTURE RECORD

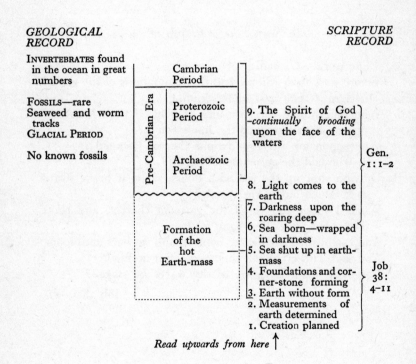

GEOLOGICAL
RECORD

SCRIPTURE
RECORD

INVERTEBRATES found in the ocean in great numbers — Cambrian Period

FOSSILS—rare
Seaweed and worm tracks
GLACIAL PERIOD — Proterozoic Period

No known fossils — Archaeozoic Period

Pre-Cambrian Era

9. The Spirit of God –continually brooding upon the face of the waters — Gen. 1:1-2

8. Light comes to the earth
7. Darkness upon the roaring deep
6. Sea born—wrapped in darkness
5. Sea shut up in earth-mass
4. Foundations and corner-stone forming
3. Earth without form
2. Measurements of earth determined
1. Creation planned — Job 38: 4-11

Formation of the hot Earth-mass

Read upwards from here ↑

THE FIRST ERA (continued):
THE FOUNDATIONS OF THE EARTH

Where wast thou when I laid the Foundations of the Earth?

THE FOUNDATIONS FOR THE HOME

At this point in our story we interrupt the Genesis sequence of events, which goes on to state that "there was darkness upon the face of the deep".

Other passages in the Hebrew writings look back also to these early days in the earth's history, and pierce behind the veil with a series of remarkable questions and statements. We shall see that the information given is so remarkable that it could come from the mouth of a modern astronomer questioning a class of students.

But first let us see what the astronomer tells us of events which followed on the establishment of the earth as a plastic mass.

Certain writers point out that as the surface of the hot earth-mass cooled an outer crust formed. From this condition the developments in and upon this primal crust can be imagined from the following statements.

THE CRUST AND ITS SUPPORTS

One modern writer, viewing the upper portion of the completed crust—the one upon which we now dwell—speaks of it as a sedimentary carpet, well-worn and ragged in parts but supported largely by a floor of granitic rocks in the continental areas. He estimates that the floor would measure up to 20 miles in thickness.(14) It is thought that under this there is another region of mixed iron and silicate rocks, the radius of which might measure from 1,000 to 2,000 miles. Again, this would merge into a very dense central core composed possibly of nickel-iron, the radius of which would be anything between 2,000–3,000 miles.

Having looked at this interesting, though somewhat vague information presented to us by the scientist, let us now consider

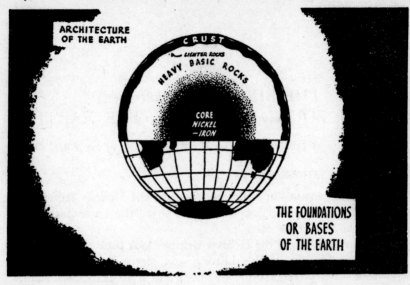

ARCHITECTURE OF THE EARTH

THE FOUNDATIONS OR BASES OF THE EARTH

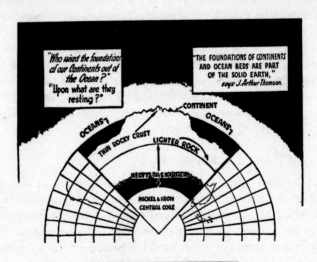

"Where wast thou when I laid the foundations of the earth" (Job 38: 4).

what the sacred Authority has to say about the earth's "foundations". To get the complete Bible presentation about the history of the early earth we pass to the Book of Job, where we obtain some picturesque details from One who not only witnessed events as its Architect but who has taken us into His confidence concerning some of the problems He had to consider when planning the world. No other book possesses such a unique and original account. The amazing thing about some of the details is that much the same picture has been supplied by our scientists.

In the Sixth Era man was brought into being—created in the image of his Creator—man with a brain to think, plan and build great works. It was ordained that he should live upon this sphere for many centuries. He was to have a home with other creatures upon a world in space, with its own air supply, and materials to provide regular food supplies from season to season and generation to generation. He was also provided with oceans of water on which to travel, either in his frail bark boats or in his palatial liners.

THE IMMENSE WEIGHT OF THE OCEAN

But oceans of water are heavy. It has been estimated that the content of the oceans is 335 million cubic miles, and *one cubic mile of water* is said to weigh about 4,200 million tons. If we consider these figures, we will get some idea of the tremendous weight of water which must be pressing down upon the crust underneath the sea. However, lest we be too concerned about this matter, the geologist points out that there exists a floor of very heavy basaltic material beneath the ocean beds. Is it any wonder God asked Job and his companions where they were when He designed and prepared the foundations of the earth? We should be glad that men had no hand in these, for men learn largely by trial and error, and what a lot of peculiar worlds would have been fashioned before men got real solid foundations into the future home.

> **"Who determined the measures thereof?"** (Job 38: 5).

THE HOME—PREDETERMINED VITAL MEASUREMENTS

When an architect is asked to plan a house, the question of size is a vital one, and some of the important questions he wants to ask are: What size is it to be? How many rooms are required? How many people are to live in it? After referring Job and his friends to the foundations of the earth, the Great Architect confronted them with the very important matter of measurements. This suggests that certain measurements were rather vital. Have you ever considered the fact that God worked to a determined plan? The data now provided by modern scientists reveals the amazing fact that there must have been some very careful and precise planning. We will consider interesting facts that the Architect of the earth had to determine at the beginning of its creation.

(1) If human beings like ourselves are to live upon a sphere in space we have been informed that this sphere cannot be any random size. There must be distinct limitations to its size because of—

(*a*) the enormous quantities of water-vapour and other gasses emitted from such spheres in their early hot condition;
(*b*) the influence of gravity from spheres such as the sun and moon, because of their size;
(*c*) the influence of these spheres because of their distance from the earth.

The Earth's Size Determined Its Atmosphere

We shall see presently when considering the birth of the oceanic waters that the hot, newly born earth for a long period thew off great quantities of gas and water vapour.(16) Now the ultimate measurement of the earth's atmosphere and ocean was predetermined by the size of its earth-mass, which continually threw off in the cooling process the vapours and gases out of which the atmosphere and ocean were composed.

We can use a very simple illustration to help us visualise what this fact means. A small juicy orange measuring only $2\frac{1}{4}$ inches in diameter, when squeezed, gave about 1 oz. of liquid, but another orange measuring $3\frac{1}{4}$ inches in diameter gave about $3\frac{1}{2}$ oz. of liquid. The orange with the extra inch of diameter gave an extra two and a half ounces of liquid. Now apply this fact to the earth and the larger planets.

Seeing that the earth's ocean resulted from the water-vapour given out from its early hot mass, we can imagine the tremendous amount of water-vapour that came from the great mass of the planet Jupiter which is 1,300 times the volume of our earth and is said to have about 150 times as much sea. Later on we shall note more facts about the size of our ocean, but this is enough for the present to make us realise that to the Architect of the earth the quantity of water in its atmosphere and ocean was a very vital matter, and was to influence greatly the kind of living things that were to inhabit it.

Planets the size of Jupiter and Saturn, when hot, gave off such huge quantities of water-vapour that their land masses are said to lie buried beneath tremendous depths of ice or water.

(2) The earth has a diameter of approximately 8,000 miles. If the diameter had been the same as that of the much larger planets Jupiter or Saturn, human beings like ourselves, designed for an atmospheric pressure of approximately 15 lb. to the square inch at sea level, would not be able to withstand the tremendous pressure of many *tons* to the square inch such as the atmosphere of these planets mentioned are said to possess.(17)

SCIENCE AND THE BIBLE

It might be as well to notice here the record of another ancient Bible writer. One could almost imagine he had been reading some of the modern scientific textbooks, for, when speaking of these vital measurements, he says:

"Behold the Lord God . . . Who hath measured the waters in the hollow of His hand, and meted out heaven with a span, and comprehended the dust of the earth in a measure, and weighed the mountains in scales, and the hills in a balance?" (Isa. 40: 12).

THE HOME—THE INFLUENCE OF SPACE NEIGHBOURS

(3) Other limitations have also to be considered, viz., the relative positions of the earth, sun and moon. Some of these measurements are vital. For instance, the earth is about 240,000 miles away from the moon. The moon and the sun attract the water of the oceans and cause an average tide of about 30 feet. But Sir James Jeans informs us that if the moon were as large as the

earth and only, say, 8,000 miles away, the "pull" from the moon would cause tides on the earth hundreds of miles high, and these would flood the continents twice daily. A smaller flood with a tide half a mile high would result if we had a moon as big as the earth and in its present position.(18) Who determined the distance between the earth and the moon? And who determined the size of the moon?

(4) Another interesting fact faces us. The moon is one of the smallest heavenly bodies. It was so small at its birth that it was unable to retain its own gases and water-vapour.(19) The moon now has neither air nor water. But that is exactly what the Great Designer planned. The Psalmist says He appointed the moon for sessons (Ps. 104: 19 and Gen. 1: 14).

A MOON– THE SIZE OF THE EARTH

If the moon had been as big as the earth, it, like the earth, would have retained its water and atmosphere, and clouds would have obscured its present reflective surface, and the various monthly phases upon which the ancient inhabitants of the earth depended before the advent of the printed calendar might have been visible only occasionally, if at all. The small size of the moon, then, was carefully planned by its Architect so that the surface would reflect, without the interruption of clouds, the various phases of a regularly appointed time-table for the benefit of earth dwellers.

(5) Let us look at other facts. The earth is about 91 million miles away from the sun. We are informed by the scientists that if our sun were removed to 120 million miles away the inhabitants of the earth would freeze, and if the sun were only 60 million miles away we and the vegetation on the earth would be burnt.

(6) Modern scientists go further. They tell us that there are in the heavens spheres known as super-suns, and if the world had one of these super-suns in the position of our present sun the earth would become so hot that it would vaporise into gas.(20) Let me provide you with the exact quotation:(20A)

"There are some brilliant stars about 10,000 times as bright as our sun. Each of them sends out in a few minutes as much radiant heat as the sun puts out in the year. If our sun were as bright as one of these stars, the temperature of the earth would vaporise into its component atoms."

Now, perhaps, we are beginning to understand why God, the Great Architect, asked Job the first question:

"WHO . . . DETERMINED [THESE VITAL] MEASURE-MENTS?"

The shields of the upper crust according to Professor J. W. Gregory.

"Whereupon are the founda-tions [bases] sunk" (Job 38: 6).

THE HOME—THE DEEP FOUNDATIONS

With this question the Great Architect again challenges Job and his friends. A free translation could read: "Upon what deep supports rests the foundations of our continents?" Books on geology will now help our thinking.

One writer has spoken of the surface of the earth as being likened to a carpet composed largely of sedimentary rocks; that is, those that have been formed from the very small particles eroded from rocks and carried along as sediment by the action of running water, later on to be deposited in the quietness of a lake or ocean.

Professor Gregory has informed us that with these sedimentary rocks there are scattered over the surface of the earth about seven very large massive blocks known as "shields" or "massifs" and which he has been pleased to call "cornerstones".(21) They belong to the upper crust and are situated in North and South America, Sweden, Siberia, India, Africa and Australia. These huge massive areas of rock existed from early times, and the Professor tells us that the present continental areas were largely built around them and they influenced the building of the later chains of mountains.

We can therefore imagine this sedimentary carpet during the geological ages being pushed, torn aside and folded, but eventually upon its surface man laboured, ploughed and reaped his harvests of food. But a carpet is placed upon a floor, and even continental areas must rest upon some foundation. The geologist would therefore take us deeper and reveal the immediate supports for these large continental areas. Here is what one well-known authority has to say upon this:(22)

"These oldest rocks—that form the basement of continental land-masses—often cover large areas, and are spoken of as 'massifs', 'coigns' or 'shields'. . . . Australia, like the other continents, rests upon a basement-complex of Pre-Cambrian rocks. . . . We are here face to face with . . . the very floor of the continent, a foundation 'massif' on which the newer sediments have been built up during the succeeding geological periods. . . . The sediments, which at first were soft, when subjected to crush and super-heated conditions of a later age, became crystalline, and passed into fusion. Granites formed in the folds of the mountain ranges. . . . These were the days during which the foundations of the continents were laid, but how profoundly distant that age."

We are to understand from the research worker that our continents are resting upon a granitic mass which has a density of about 2.65. Below this there are basic rocks containing yet denser materials. Going yet deeper through these successive shells we eventually arrive at the central core, which is generally believed to consist of iron and nickel, having a density of about 10. This high density is believed to be caused by the enormous pressures involved.

It is worth recording here that the Hebrew word that has been translated "fastened" (whereupon are the foundations fastened) can mean "sunk", so that the general idea could mean that these foundations or supports were sunk deeply on the inside of the sphere. Indeed, one Hebrew lexicon says: "It is used of the pedestals of the earth as settled or planted."

With these scientific facts and theories in mind we may be able to understand better why God challenged Job with this question about the earth's foundations. However, another scripture reference becomes very interesting here: "He hath founded the earth upon her bases that it should not be removed forever" (Ps. 104: 5).

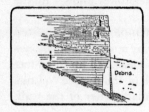
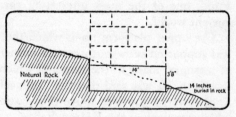

The cornerstone at the south-east portion of Solomon's temple and (lower) the cornerstone of the Earth.

"Who laid the cornerstone thereof?" (Job 38: 6).

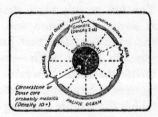

THE VITAL CORNERSTONE

Various people have suggested that the Old Testament writers had much the same idea as their heathen neighbours, viz., that they thought of the earth as something that was flat and supported somehow from underneath by elephants or pillars or Atlas.

In these questions put to Job we are faced with the fact that this cornerstone evidently had something to do with the deep supports of the crust. Now Webster's Dictionary defines a cornerstone as "one that is part of a corner or angle of a wall, especially one lying at the foundation of a principal angle". Our authority says further: "Figuratively it is something of fundamental importance."

But where are we to locate a cornerstone on a spherical body such as our earth? How are we to interpret this question so that it will be in agreement with the Hebrew presentation and also with modern scientific theories and findings?

Professor J. W. Gregory mentioned seven cornerstones,(23) but we have already noted that these are located upon the surface of the crust and therefore they cannot be considered as being a deeply buried single unit, as this phrase and its context demands.

Perhaps an illustration from the wall of the temple built by Solomon may help us. There was located by excavators in the last century, under the supervision of the Palestine Exploration Fund, one of the most interesting cornerstones known in the ancient world.

The upper platform upon which the temple buildings rested was supported at its south-eastern corner by a number of courses of masonry, many of the stones of which measured up to 20 feet in length. It was said that the "pinnacle of the temple" (Luke 4: 9) towered 300 feet above this particular corner of the wall, which overlooked the Kidron Valley.

Now the builders of this wall were faced with a problem. The hill at this place descended very steeply into the valley. A strong foundation was therefore necessary, and there was the additional fact that just at this position there was to be a junction of two walls—one looking southwards and the other facing the east. It was to be a very vital corner, taking many courses of large stones before a platform could be erected, upon which the temple building would be supported.

Solomon's builders were quite equal to the task set them. The excavators found that a unique stone had been cut and placed into position at this south-eastern angle. It was 14 feet long and 3 feet 8 inches at the corner angle, but it was noted that this large stone had been let down into the native rock of the hill to a depth of 14 inches at the corner, while at its 14 foot end it was entirely buried in the rock which had been cut to receive it.

Now before Job was asked the question, "Who laid the corner-stone" (of the earth), he was reminded of its foundations or bases which were buried deeply. We have already noted, too, how the scientists seek to probe deeper and deeper into the secrets of the earth until they visualise an inner core at which the enormous pressures make them think of a density of 10 for a substance thought to be composed of nickel-iron.

The Bible student can therefore visualise a cornerstone indeed. Situated at the deepest base reached from any part of the earth there is a central core. Lines drawn from any point of the outside crust through the centre reveal angles which meet upon this most important core or cornerstone of the earth. Now we can understand something of the challenge God put to Job, when he asked, "Who laid the cornerstone?"

Where did the sea come from?

> "Who shut up the sea with
> doors?" (Job. 38: 6).

THE OCEAN—ITS BIRTH-PLACE

This most pertinent question, again directed to Job and his
friends, opens up quite a series of very interesting scientific
facts. Ask a scientist who has followed the subject: "Where did
the sea come from?" and a very fascinating talk will result.
The writer once put this question to a friend, and he smiled and
said: "That's an easy one."

Here is one of the scientific explanations about this event.
When the earth-mass was in its very hot condition—previously
described in the Genesis account as being "without form and
void"—tremendous quantities of gases belched out from thousands of volcano-like vents. The study of modern volcanoes
reveals the fact that with the gases that are thrown into the
atmosphere, there is a great amount of water-vapour. In the beginning the water-vapour burst forth into space and later condensed and filled the ocean beds.(24) But we must remember that
it was at first "shut up" (to use the idea given in the Bible) "with
doors" in the hot earth-mass.

> "When it [the sea] brake forth
> as it issued out of the womb"
> (Job 38: 8).

THE OCEAN—ITS MYSTERIOUS BEGINNING

From the information supplied by our scientific friends we
have already noted that the earth-mass, as it cooled, formed an
early crust, perhaps from the lighter "slag" and other materials
which collected upon the surface.(25) For a while this primal
surface-crust held back these hot gases within the mass, but they
finally burst through the crust and filled space for many miles

D

above the earth. It is thought that later on, when the temperature
fell below 700°F., the water-vapour condensed and filled the hot
ocean-beds,(26) only to rise again and again until the crust itself
eventually cooled. Wells and Huxley give us a splendid picture
of this early condition.(27) But the strange thing is that although
the ocean's birth was first recorded so admirably, picturesquely,
and scientifically in the Bible, very few people noted the fact,
or gave the Bible or its writers credit for its ancient and accurate
presentation.

Job's description of the early earth swaddled by darkness is scientifically
correct.

"When I made the cloud the
garment thereof and thick
darkness a swaddling band
for it" (Job 38: 9).

THE OCEAN—ITS EARLY CLOTHING

Scientific writers, when describing the events of the primeval
period, paint a remarkable picture, fundamentally similar to the
one in the Bible. We have seen that many gases, some light in
density, and others not so light, accompanied the rising vapours.
From tens of thousands of craters belched out these gases and
vapours, and naturally they formed a cloud of very thick gloomy
darkness which settled around the whole hot earth-mass. We
can well understand that it was not possible for the sun's light to
penetrate this awful, gloomy darkness.

Here is a picture as presented by one of the leading Australian
scientists of a past generation:(27A)

"In the early part of primeval times the observer would have seen
the earth surrounded by a thick steamy atmosphere, through occa-

sional breaks in which he might have seen a red glow from the heated surface of the earth just as the glow of hot lava from an active volcano may be seen through rifts in the clouds."

What a delightful picturesque presentation the Scripture writer made of this event. Let us forget the question how old the Book of Job may be—there have been too many pitfalls over such technicalities in the past. Let us ponder the picture itself. The infant ocean, as vapour, bursting out of Nature's womb, had its clothing waiting for it; in fact, it accompanied its birth.(28) The gloomy darkness of its clothing Job described as "a swaddling band". This eastern picture of the ocean as an infant, with hands, feet and everything tightly swaddled (excepting, of course, its yell), is complete and beautifully scientific. If we are seeking Truth we will consider well this presentation and its implications, for who could have pictured it so accurately for us except the Amazing Architect Himself?

> "And established my decree
> . . . and said, Hitherto shalt
> thou come but no further, and
> here shall thy proud waves
> be stayed" (Job 38: 10–11,
> margin).

THE OCEAN—ITS EARLY DOMINATION

But the writer of the Book of Job has not quite finished his story! There is a further interesting fact which must not be left out if the scientific picture is to be complete. The new-born infant-ocean was a very healthy one, and so important was it, even in infancy, that it is presented to us poetically as being "proud". The reason for this pride is apparent to every scientist. We are told by them that the early ocean dominated the earth. Of course, the present continents had not developed as we know them today. Their foundations were only forming. We are now informed that if we were to use giant bulldozers and completely level off the whole of the earth's present land surfaces our continental masses would be about *one to two miles under the ocean.*

Is there not cause for us to wonder that in these four most pertinent questions which the Great Architect put to Job are facts that have long been regarded only as the discoveries of proud modern minds? In an age when we hear so much about Babylonian traditions and myths, have we not cause to wonder when we discover that two other Scripture writers record the fact of a restraint which was placed upon the lusty, young ocean. As we ponder Proverbs 8: 29 and Psalm 104: 8-9 (marginal reference) let us wonder and worship.

Summary

So that we may not lose the full significance of the valuable material presented by the Book of Job, let us gather together the points commented upon. It will impress our minds better if we review this ancient testimony, which has anticipated our modern research.

1. The earth hangs (in space) upon nothing.   Job 26: 7.
2. The measurements of the earth were not the product of chance evolution, but were predetermined by the Architect.   Job 38: 5.
3. The foundations were laid by God.   Job 38: 4.
4. They were *sunk deeply* into the earth.   Job 38: 6.
5. The ocean was first "shut up" (within the earth mass).   Job 38: 8.
6. At its birth it burst forth (as vapour).   Job 38: 8.
7. It was clothed with thick darkness,   Job 38: 9.
8. which was wrapped around it as a swaddling band.   Job 38: 9.
9. The new-born ocean was proud.   Job 38: 11.
10. It had to be restrained and its boundaries fixed.   Job 38: 11.

BIBLIOGRAPHY

14. *Earth Lore*, pp. 55–71, S. J. Shand, 1937. **16.** Ref. as (13), p. 25. **17.** Ref. as (13), pp. 79–80. **18.** Ref. as (2), p. 138. **19.** *The Atmosphere, Its Design and Significance in Creation*, Transactions of Victoria Inst. vol. lxxi, p. 39, F. T. Farmer. **20.** Correspondence Canberra Observatory. **20A.** *Science Digest.* **21.** "The Making of the Earth", (*Encyclopaedia of Modern Knowledge*), pp. 192–3, J. W. Gregory,

D.Sc. **22.** *The Building of Australia*, part i, p. 32, Prof. W. Howchin. **23.** Ref. as (21), p. 192. **24.** *The Science of Life*, vol. ii, p. 432, Wells and Huxley. **25.** Ref. as (24), p. 432. **26.** Ref. as (13), p. 26. **27.** Ref. as (24), p. 432 **27A.** Ref. as (21), p. 196. **28.** Ref. as (19), p. 42.

THE FIRST ERA (*continued*):
LET THERE BE LIGHT

(*Refer to bottom of Tables* A *and* B)

"And darkness was upon the face of the [roaring] deep.

And the Spirit of God was brooding [as a bird does over its nest] continually upon the face of the waters.

And God said, Let there be light: and there was light. And God saw the light, that it was good; and God divided between the light and the darkness, and God called the light Day, and the darkness he called Night.

And there was evening and there was morning, the First Day."

Genesis 1: 2-5.

THE FIRST ERA (*continued*): LET THERE BE LIGHT

The Genesis picture of darkness upon an early turbulent ocean is also scientifically correct.

> **"And darkness was upon the face of the [roaring] deep"** (Gen. 1:2, literal).

THE OCEAN—ITS UNSETTLED CONDITION

Having read in the Book of Job the Architect's version of the structural necessities for man's future dwelling-place—its measurements, foundations and cornerstone with picturesque details of the ocean's birth, early clothing and restraint—let us now return to our first authority and consider further details of its development.

The Genesis writer, who previously told us about the unformed and unfurnished condition of the dwelling site, is now going to supply us with some very interesting details about the furnishings of the home, and will also proceed to describe the various occupants, and in the same order of arrival as that tabulated by geologists and palaeontologists.

The Architect, looking into the future, had to make provision for the feeding and comfort of a multitudinous number of people and animals, so various types of vegetation with permanent automatic watering and air-conditioning systems had to be provided. The diverse creatures which were to inhabit the waters and spacious grounds were to have their physical and economic needs carefully planned; and in order that the outlook would not become too monotonous, mountains and hills, rivers and lakes were introduced into the landscape, adding beauty and variety.

GEOLOGY REVEALS CREATIVE PROCESSES

The business of the Genesis writer was first to introduce us to the Architect, and then to set down in broad outline His creative plan and its progressive development. The task of the geologist and his companions is to show some of the intricate processes by which the Creator worked out His plan. Without the painstaking efforts and discoveries of the scientists, we would be ignorant of some of the extremely interesting details and processes by which He worked, and also much of the life which He created, particularly in the early eras.

What a tremendous amount of ink and hot air could have been saved by modern writers had they only linked Job's account to that of Genesis! Both sacred writers supplement each other and anticipate by centuries the pronouncements of scientists and the findings of geologists. We must ever remember, however, that it has been the patient work of the scientists that has filled in a tremendous amount of detail concerning the early ages and its life and also corrected certain wrong interpretations of some of the theologians.

THE OCEAN—WAS DARK AND TURBULENT

The Genesis story, however, now presents us with a very interesting fact. We are told that the Hebrew text implies that the "deep" became "turbulent" or "roaring". We have already seen from the Job narrative that the water-vapours condensed and filled the ocean beds. But in the Genesis account the earth-mass was still hot, "darkness was upon the face of the [roaring] deep", and we can imagine perhaps a boiling ocean with enormous clouds of heavy gases rising continually. The thunder and lightning and intense darkness which belonged to this period would have been terrifying indeed.

It is essential for us to understand here that the sun was never absent from its place in the heavens. It was, however, unable to penetrate the thick darkness of vapours which "swaddled" the earth. It is, therefore, not surprising that some of the ancients and not a few moderns used the idea of "chaos" when writing of this period, as no doubt the earth seemed chaotic and God-forsaken. Possibly its intense and gloomy darkness made it appear as an habitation and battleground of fiends. But we shall see presently that this idea was far from the truth.

How the scientist explains the change over from darkness to light.

"And God said, Let there be light" (Gen. 1:3).

The Home—Its Majestic Lighting System

The scientists would now have us understand that with the continued cooling of the crust eventually the rising clouds of gas and vapours ceased, and there came a time when the sun was able to shine through to the earth. The geologists point out certain things which help us to understand God's methods at the conclusion of the long centuries of darkness.

Before the great burst of life, which has been manifested in the fossils of the Cambrian Period, geologists note that large portions of the earth had a glacial period. It is also suggestive that in the period before this great burst of marine life a cooling of the crust was necessary. Speaking on this Professor J. W. Gregory says:

"The cloud belt which surrounded the early earth was removed by chilling and condensation."(29)

> "And God divided between the
> light and between the darkness
> God called the light day and
> the darkness he called night"
> (Gen. 1: 4–5, marginal).

AUTOMATIC CONTROLS WITH THE LIGHTING SYSTEMS

The illustration provided below should help us to understand
the text. First notice that the more exact marginal translation has
been used because it gives a better idea of the Hebrew. The words
of the English Authorised Version—"God divided the light
from the darkness"— are apt to confuse us, but the literal translation of the Hebrew makes a perfect picture. If previously we
have doubted that the light mentioned in Genesis, chapter 1,
was from the sun, we will surely have no doubts now. What we
were taught as children in early geography lessons now helps us
to understand things more clearly. The reference in the Gospel
of John to the darkness and the light (John 1: 1–5) is particularly
interesting.

The literal Hebrew expresses a simple picture which again is scientifically correct.

> "And the spirit of God was
> brooding [continually] [as a
> bird does over its nest] upon
> the face of the waters" (Gen.
> 1: 2, literal Hebrew).

THE HOME—ANTICIPATING THE FIRST LIFE

The Spirit of God, who was "brooding" over the waters to
establish them and to disperse the darkness, was also busy to
produce life. At this point we must stop for a moment to give a

few simple ideas about geological periods. The scientists distinguish the main divisions in the world's geological story, known as eras, as follows:

Archaeozoic, Proterozoic (era before ancient life), Palaeozoic (the era of ancient life) Mesozoic (the era of the middle forms of life), Cainozoic (era of new forms of life). They then sub-divide these large eras into many smaller sections called periods.

In the earliest times, when the foundations of the earth were laid down, we have the Archaeozoic rocks. Following these we have the Proterozoic rocks. There are no fossils from these earliest rocks apart from some rather uncertain indications shown in the Proterozoic.

When, however, we come into the Palaeozoic Era (see Table A or B), which is subdivided into six periods, known as Cambrian, Ordovician, Silurian, Devonian, Carboniferous and Permian, we find in its first period (the Cambrian) an entirely new picture.

CERTAIN EARLY LIFE WAS SPECIALISED

The Cambrian introduces us to a wonderful period of creative activity and an abundance of highly specialised marine life made its appearance (without, up to the present time, revealing precursors).(30) This early life was varied, and consisted of seaweed, jellyfish, sponges, marine worms, starfish, shell-fish, and peculiar creatures known as trilobites.

As the Palaeozoic Era proceeded new forms of marine life arrived such as corals, graptolites, vertebrates (fish and other animals with backbones), while insects and vegetation appeared upon the land.

The theory of many scientists is that life must have evolved by chance from early simple forms, and that later these became more complex and specialised.(31) But the fossil discoveries do not substantiate this theory! Instead of the earliest-known fossils showing a gradual advance from primitive forms and species to later specialised types, actual fossil evidence reveals that specialised types of life arrived, apparently very suddenly, from the Cambrian Period onwards, and the connecting fossil "links" between these widely separated groups of life cannot be located.

WORLD-WIDE SEARCH FOR PRECURSORS

Professor Percy Raymond, of Harvard, has informed us that students of geology have for a number of years made extensive searches throughout the world for precursors of these different types of early life, but up to the present none has been found. The only certain pre-Cambrian fossils which have been noted are those of marine plants (algae) and worm tracks. While claims have been made about other types of life from time to time, these have been disputed.(32)

Let us now see what some scientific authorities have to say about the problem created by the arrival of this early and varied life of the ocean. Professor James Dana, speaking of it, said:(33)

"They are perfect of their kind and highly specialised structures. No steps from simple kinds leading up to them have been discovered. This appearance of abruptness of Cambrian life is one of the striking facts made known by geology."

Again, Professor Percy Raymond, referring to the fossils, tells us that 455 species have been identified in the Lower Cambrian, and adds:(34)

"It is evident that the oldest Cambrian fauna is diversified and not so simple, perhaps, as the evolutionists would hope to find it. . . . We are not driven to a belief in an ancient special creation but further research."

Suggesting some of the diverse types of marine life belonging to the Cambrian Period.

THE FIRST LIFE WAS DIVERSIFIED

So that we may realise the full force of the fossil evidence, let me summarise what some of the leading geologists and others

have written about the first life which lived in the waters of the
Cambrian Period:

1. "The era of ancient life arrived abruptly and without
   warning" (Wells and Huxley).(35)
2. It was "highly organised and differentiated" (Howchin).(36)
3. "Diversified, and not so simple as the evolutionist would
   hope to find it" (Percy Raymond).(37)
4. "They have not the simplicity of structure that would
   naturally be looked for" (Dana).(38)
5. "They are perfect of their kind, and highly specialised
   structures" (Dana).(39)
6. There are "no steps from simple kinds leading up to
   corals, echinoderms, or worms" (Dana).(40)
7. Nor steps from these groups up to brachippods, mollusks,
   trilobites, or crustaceans (Dana).
8. "The creationists seem to have the better of the argument" (Clark).(42)
9. The fauna of the Cambrian "was in essentially the same
   form as that in which we now know it" (Clark).(43)
10. They are most intensely modern themselves in the zoo-
    logical sense (Brooks).(44)

Where Did Life Come From?

It is admitted by modern scientists that they are unable to say
HOW life came to the earth. It is also an enigma to them that
a great burst of diversified life should be found in the waters
of the Cambrian Period without first revealing its many connecting precursors.

Messrs. Wells and Huxley also looked at the difficulty caused
by the silence of the fossil record and the sudden appearance
of specialised life, and because the fossil evidence did not agree
with the theory which demanded slow organic modification and
evolutional progress they made a "tentative" and "speculative"
bridge out of comparative anatomy and embryology to span a
time gap usually estimated by geologists of at least 500 million
years.(45)

It will help our thinking, perhaps, if just here we look at a
quotation from another writer whose work appears in the very
popular, cheap and informative Pelican series:(45A)

"Anyone can see that honey bees are much like bumble bees, that bees resemble flies more than they do spiders, and that spiders are more like lobsters, than like clams. But when we attempt to relate phyla, which by definition are groups of animals with fundamentally different body plans, there is little we can say with certainty . . . the fossil record . . . is of practically no use in relating the phyla to each other."

THE SPIRIT OF GOD—THE SOURCE OF ALL LIFE

We who believe in the Great Architect of the Geological Ages see no difficulty whatever in the sudden arrival of diversified life in any geological period. The Genesis writer has given us a very positive answer to the question, "From whence did life come?"

It is extremely interesting to examine this Scripture statement, a literal translation of which is given at the head of this section. The sacred writer does not attempt to supply any data as to WHEN the Spirit of God actually introduced life into the waters. The picture portrayed allows for life at any time the waters were ready to receive it, and the fossil record, contained in the Books of the Rocks will be the authority to which we can appeal on this interesting point.

The picture revealed by the Hebrew is very suggestive and picturesque. A bird first searches around and gradually gathers together the heavier sticks and twigs for the frame of its nest. Then it gathers the lighter material, as well as hair and downy feathers, for the inside lining. Later on, when the nest is completed, the eggs are deposited and the warmth of the bird's body conveyed to the eggs. In due course the young life appears.

CONTINUITY OF BROODING UPON THE WATERS

Hebrew scholars point out that even this splendid picture does not do justice to the text. The English translator's continual use of the word "and" throughout the early verses in the Authorised text was an attempt to convey the idea of continuity of action, a continuity which lasted throughout long geological eras. All the time when the earth was unformed and void of life—all the time of the so-called chaos, when the darkness was upon the face of the deep—during this long period *the Spirit of God hovered or brooded continually, just as a bird does over its nest.* In other words, all that time, which man has described as chaotic, the

All-wise Creator was superintending the processes by His Spirit of Wisdom: the hot earth-mass with its projections and deep foundations, the ocean's birth and restraint, and the cooling process. The warmth of the sun upon the waters continued the process. So the Spirit of God watched and worked continually, throughout the long Palaeozoic Era, until the time came when the Architect could pronounce the work "good".

The picture of the brooding bird, as supplied by the Hebrew text, gives a clue which suggests to us how the early Phoenicians and others possibly came to believe that all life came from an egg. However, let us not forget the fact that the Hebrew writer has placed this most illuminating phrase in his statement of creation, just at that position where, in the geological column, the scientists are most anxiously searching for an explanation for the abundant varied and specialised life that is manifest in the early fossil record of the Palaeozoic Era.

THE PASTURES OF THE SEA

In the early part of the twentieth century it was suggested by certain writers that the earliest life of the ocean may have been a "jelly-like" substance. It was even suggested that this jelly-like material may have been the first-born life of the ocean out of which other life somehow gradually evolved.

There has been a great amount of biological research, particularly in Britain, upon the matter of very small jelly-like marine life which is given the general name of Plankton. Now this material consists of the eggs and very young life of many species of very small marine animals, including single-celled life.

On one occasion one very enthusiastic writer referred to the fact that the time might not be far distant when acres of the sea might be worth just as much as pastoral acres on the land. His point was that marine life of all kinds must have food, and therefore marine pastures are just as necessary as terrestrial.

SINGLE-CELLED LIFE IS COMPLEX

It has been found by these patient research workers that the single-celled marine plant or animal is not to be despised, firstly, because if we are to have higher orders of life such as fish, then food must be available for them. Naturally like that which is

E

provided in the terrestrial pastures, this food need not be of a relatively complex type, but it must be of such a nature that it will multiply rapidly whether in a small pond or in a great ocean.

At one time the single-celled amoeba of the pond was just written down as being a more-or-less bit of low-down-the-scale-jelly-like material, and perhaps it is, but what most text-books previously omitted to inform their readers was that these single-celled individuals which multiplied at such an amazing rate were part of the pastures of the waters, whether pond or sea. After all, the Designer's viewpoint as to the *food value* of the thing does not seem to have been advertised as much as the fact that it was merely a low-down single-celled bit of life that provided the evolutionist with a starting point for his theory.

The Wonders of Amoeba

The modern research worker, however, has become rather loud in his praise of amoeba and his tribal associates. Sketches made in text-books reveal a rather complex individual. An amoeba, even though single-celled, multiplies in a very amazing way.(46) It can reproduce its kind under favourable circumstances until they number many thousands per day. Its method of reproduction proclaims to us that there must be some kind of machine-like control, but when a thing reproduces itself consistently age after age, then it seems to argue that the very intelligent Designer created the machine for some purpose.

But this is not all. Using the amoeba as being one representative of a tremendous host, we find that the amoeba can swim, it can thrust out its jelly-like body in any direction, it lays hold of its food and absorbs it. It evidently digests what it can and rejects what it cannot. It breathes. If you destroy its nucleus it dies, when drought comes to a pond, and an amoeba is in danger of becoming extinct, then a cist is built somehow automatically, and this low-down-the-scale single-celled bit of protoplasm lies dormant in the mud and awaits the arrival of water so that it may keep on living and become the food designed for the animals that cannot live outside of the element they were created for. Now we can see the necessity for the Designer providing for food the simple forms of life in the waters of the world because there were to be many other complex and higher forms needing food.

LIFE IN A CORAL POOL

For the benefit of those folk who enjoy reading the evidence of the Great Designer's work, let me give a few illustrations that are in keeping with the subject under review.

I have had the great pleasure on several occasions of visiting many of the delightful colourful coral pools associated with the Great Barrier Reef off the coast of North Queensland. I know nothing on this earth that equals the exquisite colour and arrangement of these beautiful coral pools and the life associated with them. On the last occasion I had the good fortune to read a report from the leader of a recent scientific expedition that visited the reef to study its abundant marine life. I would like to quote much more from this report, but space will permit but a few references.

Speaking of the manner in which corals live, the writer first remarks that food is the first essential, and then says the following:(47)

"In spite of their beautiful flower-like appearance, corals are carnivorous animals, to approach too near to which is death to the minute animal life (plankton) of the sea. The tentacles which wave with such grace carry batteries of minute but deadly weapons, known as nettle-cells. These, though microscopic in size, are most elaborate in structure, consisting of an oval-shaped bag, within which, bathed in poisonous fluid, lies the finest of coiled springs. The spring is shot out as a long barbed thread, which enters the body of the (microscopic) animal causing instant paralysis. Each tentacle bears many thousands of these nettle-cells, and so is a most deadly weapon."

PLANTS AND ANIMALS NEED EACH OTHER

The same writer then goes on to describe a countless number of very minute brown bodies which live within the corals themselves. He says that these are *microscopic plants* of a very simple type. The business of these plants is to supply oxygen to the corals. The plants need the carbonic acid gas which is given out by the (coral) animals. On the other hand, the animals (corals) need the oxygen which is produced by the plants. He says:(47)

"Give the plants a free hand and the water would become in time so alkaline as to destroy them. Give the animals a free hand and they, in the end, would be killed by the acidity they themselves produced, and so the two working against one another insure the maintenance of conditions vital to both.

"All life is like that, a thousand inter-acting and balanced forces, like the flying buttresses of a towering Gothic Cathedral; destroy one and the whole graceful fabric comes down in irreparable ruin."

A final interesting fact is mentioned about this microscopic life. The animals that form this group are very sensitive to light, each particular kind having apparently a definite sensitivity to light that suits it best. During the absence of light at night there is nothing to control their position in the water, and they spread out through the various layers. As dawn breaks, and light begins to penetrate the surface waters, these move upwards, and for a short period the surface is thick with them. As the light increases with the appearance of the sun, the plankton begins to descend. Some kinds go deeper than others; each kind ceases its downward movement *when it reaches the zone of light most suited for it.*

These "pastures of the sea" are arranged in an orderly fashion, so that not only are some of the multitudinous microscopical plants and animals placed together to contribute the life-giving gases necessary for each, but the various types of plankton so react to the light that automatically they are made to rise and fall in the waters, to provide food at those positions best suited to the higher orders of life that may frequent each particular region.

FOOD DELIVERED BY SUNLIGHT

What a delightful picture of the exquisite planning of the Great Architect of the Universe this makes for us. As the sun rises for its daily task through the heavens its rays gradually reach down to the depths of the great waters.

At some of the layers, not too far below the surface, await the corals. Overnight their food supply had drifted away from them. Their homes had been built upon layer after layer of limey coral. They cannot leave these permanent structures, like other free swimming varieties of life, so they must await with patience their daily portion of food from the Great Provider.

As the light of the new day reaches beneath the surface, the process of distribution of the daily food begins. Every variety of living thing in the waters has been catered for, whether bound to rocks, or possessing freedom to move as desire dictates, and each has its food automatically placed more or less within reach of its mouth.

One wonders at the tremendous battle that would have to take place daily if all the plankton had been assigned to one level—a real struggle for daily food and existence truly! But, no, the Great Provider arranged this distribution of daily portions to the dwellers of the deep, whether their habitat was near the surface, at the bottom, or in the layers between.

To demonstrate His Wisdom further, the corals were provided with a specialised apparatus. These creatures perhaps could know a pleasure similar to that of the human hunter or angler, and so with their darts attached to living lines, their appetites were perfectly satisfied.

Not only to the dwellers in terrestrial areas does the sun bring their daily portion of food in the form of juicy fruits or succulent grasses, but the countless creatures of the great waters may know a physical pleasure by the arrival of their daily portion of food, literally delivered with the rising sun.

In the geological eras the Holy Spirit of the Living God brooded upon the face of the waters, and life was produced. Today He makes His sun to move upon the waters, and provision is made daily for the sustenance of all its multitudinous life.

BIBLIOGRAPHY

29. "The Making of the Earth" (*Encyclopaedia of Modern Knowledge*), p. 195, Prof. J. W. Gregory. **30.** *Manual of Geology*, 4th ed. p. 487, Prof. Jas. Dana. **31.** *Organic Evolution*, p. 6, Prof. R. S. Lull. **32.** *Prehistoric Life*, Prof. Raymond. **33.** Ref. as (30), p. 487. **34.** Ref. as (32). **35.** *The Science of Life*, vol. ii, p. 453, Wells and Huxley. **36.** *The Building of Australia*, vol. i, p. 42, Prcf. W. Howchin. **37.** Ref. as (32). **38.** Ref. as (33), p. 487. **39.** Ref. as (33), p. 487. **40.** Ref. as (33), p. 487. **42.** *Quarterly Review of Biology*, Smithsonian Institute, Dec. 1928, Austin H. Clark. **43.** Ref. as (42). **44.** *Foundation of Zoology*, p. 216, W. K. Brooks. **45.** Ref. as (35), p. 441-2. **45A.** *Animals Without Backbones*, vol. xi (Pelican Series), p. 363, Ralph Buchsbaum. **46.** *The Corridor of Life*, pp. 48-9, Swinton and Pinner. **47.** *A Year on the Great Barrier Reef*, C. M. Yonge, 1930.

THE SECOND ERA: THE ESTABLISHMENT OF THE ATMOSPHERE

(Refer to Tables A and C)

"And God said:
   Let there be an expanse in the midst of the waters,
   And let it divide the waters from the waters.
   And God made an expanse,
   And divided the waters which were under the expanse from
      the waters which were above the expanse; and it was
      so.
   And God called the expanse Heaven.
   And the evening and the morning were the Second Day."

Genesis 1: 6–8.

THE SECOND ERA:
THE ESTABLISHMENT OF THE ATMOSPHERE

The literal Hebrew expresses a profound fact about our atmosphere.

> **"And God said, Let there be an expanse in the midst of the waters"** (Gen. 1: 7).

THE HOME—THE VITAL AIR-CONDITIONING SYSTEM

We have seen how scientists explain the coming of water into the ocean beds. In much the same way the gases, we are told, that came from the hot earth-mass, were used to make the atmosphere. The explanation sounds simple and logical. Quite naturally the lightest gases would rise to the highest positions while the medium and heavier ones would adjust themselves on lower levels. Naturally it is impossible for scientists to explain HOW, from thousands of craters, the mixture of poisonous gases sorted themselves, so that the precise amount of life-giving oxygen so necessary for terrestrial inhabitants happened to be available when it was required. Some writers inform us that Saturn and Jupiter still have poisonous gases in large quantities.(48) Others tell us that the earth is thought to be the *only* planet with quantities of life-giving oxygen. Venus, known as the Earth's twin, has a poisonous gas in enormous quantities, while the temperature of Jupiter and Saturn is said to be lower than —150°C. (49) Not only had our atmospheric mixture

73

to be very carefully adjusted to terrestrial life, but the correct mixture of nitrogen and oxygen has to be maintained throughout the ages, or else terrestrial inhabitants would cease to exist. All these things required not only the planning of an Architect and the wisdom of a Creator but also the expert mind of One who was a very efficient manufacturing Chemist.

Some confusion has been caused by the translators of the Authorised Version using the word "firmament". Now this word, rightly or wrongly, has sometimes been given a specialised meaning. We have been told that the ancients regarded the "firmament" as being more or less a metal arch or dome in the heavens which had holes punched into it to allow the rain through. Whatever views the Babylonians or other people had at the time of Christ is no concern of ours and must not cloud the truth. We are concerned with the meaning of the word in the original language of those who wrote the Scriptures. The Hebrew word "Raqiya" comes from a root meaning to "stamp out" or in another form means "to spread out by striking". We get the idea in the noun, of something "spread out" or "stretched out" after having been fashioned by the Maker. The word expanse or atmosphere is now used as conveying this meaning. It is something spread out over the earth.

THE ATMOSPHERE IS SPREAD AS A TENT

Another idea is given in Isaiah 40: 22. Here we have the thought of the limitation of the expanse or atmosphere. It is, as a "tent, to dwell in":

"It is He . . . that stretcheth out the heavens as a curtain, and spreadeth them out as a tent to dwell in."

It is interesting to realise that our atmosphere is spread out like a blanket, or tent, around the solid earth. The following facts should therefore be of interest to us.

Our atmosphere is said to have a mass of about 5,500 million tons and this extends upward to between 200 and 300 miles. If all the atmosphere were of uniform density, as it is at sea level, it would only be about 5 miles thick, but the pressures are not uniform, and so living things cannot exist beyond about 4 miles without artificial means. When human beings go to the fringe of the "tent" or expanse of atmosphere they must take a supplementary supply of oxygen with them, or die.

The Early Adjustment of the Atmosphere

The scientifically minded person quite naturally asks if any indication can be given of the position in the geological ages when the Great Architect adjusted the atmosphere.

The first fossils of air-breathing insects occur in the Silurian Period. We can therefore recognise atmospheric stability in this period. But this fact only argues that we have here perhaps only the first conditions most suitable for the preservation of the fossils of these early air-breathing insects.

The scientist therefore looks for other evidence. In the Cambrian Period, for instance, we noted that the fossils reveal sea life such as jellyfish, sponges, worms, starfish, etc., all of which must have oxygen and which we know is found in the water of the ocean. It can therefore be argued that the atmosphere must have been stabilised before this life could exist.

This recognition, then, of the earliest adjustment of the atmosphere depends upon factors of which at present we have

These diagrams help us to understand the Biblical use of the words "expanse" and "heaven".

very little scientific evidence, but it must have been before the introduction of life into the ocean, whenever that first occurred.

The fact that the sacred writer has placed the establishment of the atmosphere in the next period, and *just after the coming of the light*, speaks very eloquently for the scientific accuracy of the Genesis record.

> "Let it divide the waters from the waters . . . and God divided the waters which were under the expanse [ocean] from the waters upon the expanse [clouds]" (Gen. 1: 7).

THE HOME—ATMOSPHERIC WATER STORAGE

The sacred writer distinguishes between two sets of waters, those which lie *underneath* the expanse or atmosphere, and those which lie *upon* the expanse. The waters underneath are, of course, the oceans. These comprise waters in a liquid form. But the atmosphere bears the load of other waters which are in a gaseous form and are carried about by the movements (wind) of the atmosphere. Some is just invisible water vapour, and some becomes visible as clouds. It is a very picturesque way of stating a simple fact to say that the expanse or atmosphere is the medium which maintains a separation between these two types of water.

Probably little thought is given by modern people to the tremendous amount of water which lies suspended invisibly over their heads. Water is continually being turned to vapour and lifted up into the atmosphere by the sun, then the wind moves that moisture over to the land areas (see Eccles. 1: 6–7). We do not always see the movement of this "water", as it is so well distributed throughout the atmosphere. The average moisture content is about 4 grains of water to a cubic foot, and it is visible in the atmosphere only when in cloud form. Commander D. J. Mares, one-time Commonwealth meteorologist in New South Wales, has given figures to illustrate this fact.(50) He estimated that in January, when the moisture content of the atmosphere over Australia is greatest, we have, floating over the whole of the Commonwealth, and unseen by human eyes, an average of 1,092 billion tons of moisture, or over a million million tons.

THE EXQUISITE PLANNING OF THE ARCHITECT

The ancient sacred writer has again anticipated our modern scientist. What lay person, ancient or modern, could imagine such an immense volume of water suspended overhead! The picturesque presentation given us by the ancient writer certainly challenges us to recognise the exquisite planning of the All-wise Architect, as well as the precision of the Hebrew writers, who recorded the fact correctly throughout the centuries, even though perhaps not quite understood by them.

However, we must not lose sight of the wisdom that we see demonstrated in the falling of this atmospheric water in the form of rain. If this tremendous ocean above our heads had not been wisely and carefully planned we might easily have had streams and floods descending upon us instead of the countless number of individual drops gently falling upon the thirsty earth, in which case soil erosion would have been a problem indeed!

BIBLIOGRAPHY

48. *The Origin of the Earth*, pp. 71–85, W. M. Smart, 1950.
49. *The Nature of the Universe*, p. 17, Hoyle. **50.** *Correspondence*.

THE THIRD ERA:
DRY LAND AND VEGETATION APPEAR

The Sacred Record—Genesis 1: 6-13

DRY LAND APPEARS

"AND GOD SAID:

Let the waters under the heaven be collected unto one place, and let the dry land appear, and it was so. And God called the dry land Earth [soil—surface of the ground] and the reservoir of the waters called he Seas, and God saw that it was good."

THE COMING OF VEGETATION

"AND GOD SAID:

Let the earth bring forth tender sproutage, the herb yielding seed after his kind and the tree yielding fruit whose seed is in itself, upon the earth: and it was so.

And the earth brought forth tender sproutage, and herb yielding seed after his kind, and the tree yeilding fruit, whose seed was in itself, after his kind: and God saw that it was good.

And the evening and the morning were the Third Day."

TABLE C

CORRELATION OF GEOLOGICAL MATERIAL WITH THE SCRIPTURE RECORDS

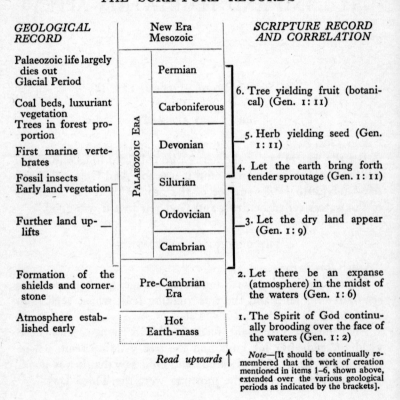

GEOLOGICAL RECORD			SCRIPTURE RECORD AND CORRELATION
	New Era Mesozoic		
Palaeozoic life largely dies out Glacial Period		Permian	
			6. Tree yielding fruit (botanical) (Gen. 1: 11)
Coal beds, luxuriant vegetation		Carboniferous	
Trees in forest proportion	PALAEOZOIC ERA	Devonian	5. Herb yielding seed (Gen. 1: 11)
First marine vertebrates			4. Let the earth bring forth tender sproutage (Gen. 1: 11)
Fossil insects Early land vegetation		Silurian	
		Ordovician	3. Let the dry land appear (Gen. 1: 9)
Further land uplifts			
		Cambrian	
Formation of the shields and cornerstone		Pre-Cambrian Era	2. Let there be an expanse (atmosphere) in the midst of the waters (Gen. 1: 6)
Atmosphere established early		Hot Earth-mass	1. The Spirit of God continually brooding over the face of the waters (Gen. 1: 2)

Read upwards ↑

Note—[It should be continually remembered that the work of creation mentioned in items 1–6, shown above, extended over the various geological periods as indicated by the brackets].

CHAPTER V

THE THIRD ERA:
DRY LAND AND VEGETATION APPEAR

> "God said, Let the waters be collected unto one place, and let the dry land appear. And God called the dry land Earth, and the reservoir of the waters called he Seas" (Gen. 1: 9–10).

THE HOME—SOIL FOR THE GARDEN

We have referred previously to the huge "coigns" which originally projected above the ocean waters. These, we are informed, gradually weathered down, and over long periods built up layers of sediment in the waters adjoining these areas. We can imagine many miles of shallow waters formed by silt brought down from these high stony areas. One writer has helped us to comprehend something of the tremendous amount of silt carried down from mountains and plains and deposited into the sea.(51) We are told that the Mississippi discharges into the Gulf of Mexico a million tons of water every minute. But the geologist illuminates this statement by informing us that the river really discharges at the same time 200 tons of dissolved lime and salts and nearly 800 tons of silt.

We can also imagine how cheap river transport would be, as against haulage by rail. Professor Salisbury has worked out that to carry and discharge such a load of mud, sand and gravel every minute of the day would be utterly beyond the capacity of any railway system in the world. He has estimated that it would require 900 trains daily, each train consisting of 50 trucks and each truck loaded to 25 tons to carry this quantity of sand and mud to the gulf.(52) When such a discharge has gone on for centuries we can well appreciate how large deltas were formed at such places as the mouths of the Nile, Euphrates, Danube and Indus rivers.

How Dry Land Formed

Very interesting observations made by geologists help us to understand the Scripture portion with which we are at present concerned. Speaking of the building of the Continent of Australia, one writer says:(53)

"Earth movements of great intensity occurred. A 'creep' in the rocks, brought about by pressure, forced the sediments into folds. These positive movements *lifted the sea floor* into dry land and mountain ranges, *and the sea retreated.*"

An English geologist has expressed himself in much the same way. He says:(53A)

"Towards the end of Cambrian times the seas began to retreat and areas of the sea floor became dry land."

And again (of Silurian times):

"In some regions there was a periodic alternation of level of land and sea; new land areas were slowly emerging and new mountain ranges were beginning to form."

The Sea Floor Lifted—The Sea Retreated

Have not these research workers given us in these phrases fundamentally the same ideas as the sacred writer who has recorded *the command* given by God:

"Let the waters be collected into one place and let the dry land appear [out of the water]."

The geologists have given us a picture of the manner in which *the command was carried out.* Notice what one says:

"These movements *lifted the sea floor into dry land* . . . *and the sea retreated.*"

Could any correlation between scientific and sacred writers living many centuries apart be expressed more perfectly?

According to the different text-books on geology it would seem that the lifting and folding of the earth's surface occurred at different periods in different parts of the world. But roughly speaking the geologists tell us that in the pre-Cambrian Ordovician and Silurian times there was a great amount of folding and earth movement before the advent of the earliest terrestrial plant life.

It should be realised, however, that in subsequent geological ages there have been further periods of land uplifting. The Genesis writer has drawn attention to the uplifting that took place in that tremendous span of time *after* the period when light first came to the earth and the atmosphere was established, and *before* the advent of land vegetation.

> **"And God said . . . Let the earth bring forth sproutage"** (Gen. 1: 11–12).

THE GARDEN—THE FIRST PLANTS ARRIVE

In a further comment our authority has mentioned another fact which reveals the delightful agreement between the two records. He says:(54)

"It was not until dry land appeared and permanent fresh-water supplies were abundant upon the earth's surface that the *plant world* found its suitable conditions by which it could develop higher structures and/or great variety of forms."

We must now pause to observe several important things even at the risk of repetition. The sacred writer and the scientist have noted the same details, even though the events took place over great spans of time, and each *has grouped them together* in their particular divisions:

(*a*) The dry land appeared out of the waters.
(*b*) The waters were collected together and formed seas.
(*c*) Vegetation of different kinds came upon the dry land.

The geologist, in checking over *God's rock records* in A.D. 1930, was constrained to mention a similar group of facts to those recorded about 1,500 B.C. in *God's Written Record*, which has so often been consigned by certain scholars to the realm of myth.

An Architect Who Delighted in Creating

We must remember that the Architect delighted in creating things. Today we find multitudinous varieties of life living under a variety of conditions in the air, in the sea and on land. It is found on and under the bark of trees, in the water of small ponds by the wayside, or in the waters of the great oceans. It can be seen under and on the rocks of the fields, or on the mountainsides.

As soon as conditions were ready for vegetation the rock records show God creating a type of life suitable to the prevailing conditions. The first types of terrestrial vegetation discovered are those which the botanists call "primitive types". Naturally we would expect the Creator to bring into being only those forms which would prosper under the hard conditions prevailing in those early periods.

The Hebrew word translated "grass" in our Authorised Version comes from a root which means "to sprout", "to shoot". In later times the word was used for ordinary grass, but, strictly, any plant that shoots out of the earth could be described as "deshe" or "sproutage". One of the earliest types of vegetation at present known to us (rhynia) had a root growth similar to our mountain bracken, and the fronds sprouted out from these roots. It was quite fitting for the writer to say: "Let the earth bring forth sproutage"; this idea is certainly supported by the discovered fossils.

> **"Herb yielding seed"** (Gen. 1: 12).

The Garden—Mechanical Reproduction

The sacred writer also described another type of vegetation, viz. plants which develop seeds. He carefully noted in the next phrase that these seeds reproduced "after their kind". It was God's purpose in His creation of living things—germs, microbes, fungi, trees, fish, mammals and men—that each variety should reproduce "after its kind". The early geological layers have *not* yet revealed fossils which show the development of land plants *from seaweeds* as desired by the evolutionist.

It might be as well to mention here that Luther Burbank, in writing about modern plants, speaks of the "miracle of the pollen".(55) He points out that we cannot fertilise apple seed with the pollen from a pear tree, nor roses with the pollen from any other plant. The Creator has placed a barrier within the pollen of each family of plants, and we cannot see in the fossil record any interbreeding between "foreign" groups of plants. However, we may use the pollen of plants in the same group or family and thus have a great variety *within a group*.

Types of carboniferous vegetation, and some of the many derivatives from coal.

"And the tree yielding fruit in which is its seed—after its kind" (Gen. 1: 12).

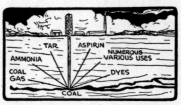

THE GARDEN—MAGICAL MULTIPLICATION

We must remember that the sacred writer when using these words was not speaking of edible fruit. Trees which have covered seeds, such as the conifers and eucalypti, bear fruit, but their fruit is not eaten. In other words, the seed of those plants is to be found inside its fruit. It is a botanical way of describing such products. Trees bearing edible fruits did not appear upon the earth until the Cretaceous Period (at the end of the Mesozoic Era). However, we will refer to this again.

Geologists provide us with the interesting fact that by Devonian times plant life had reached the proportions of forest growth,(56) and trees would measure up to 2 feet in diameter. By the Carboniferous Period we are told that some trees would measure up to 100 feet high and trunks 3 feet in diameter.

THE DIFFICULTIES OF THE EARLY SEAWEEDS

It is interesting here for us to read the information provided by those popular writers, Wells and Huxley, who, when dealing with the problems confronting those who hold the theory of evolution of plants, wrote:(57)

"Then comes a second difficulty the seaweed had to surmount before it could pass on to the grade of a land inhabitant. In the sea you never dry up; in land you are always drying up. How not to be dried up was a problem every living creature which pushed out of the waters onto the land had to solve."

Again, when dealing with the structural differences between sea and land plants, they say (brackets are author's):(58)

"These main distinctive structures are necessary to any land plant (which evolves from sea plants); that is, to grow erect, difference of root and stem, woody skeleton, and upward or downward transport systems (nourishment). We find that they had all been developed by the Middle Devonian Period. [See Table C.] Then they appear essential land plants and all the subsequent lapse of time has brought only minor variations or improvements of detail."

And here is another interesting statement from the same writers:(59)

"Many botanists believe that the threshold between sea and land has been crossed, not by one stock only of plants, but by several, and that the Jointed Plants, the Club-mosses and the Ferns, for instance, are not relatives all descended from a common land ancestor, but travelling companions who have all happened to take the same road, like land arthropod and land vertebrate."

However, lest it be thought that any undue advantage has been taken of these popular writers, here are the words of a leading botanist:(59A)

"When we get back to the Devonian Period a veil falls, and all the earlier course of evolution (immensely the greater part of the whole history) remains hidden."

DIFFICULTIES OF THE SCIENTISTS

In order to appreciate fully the difficulties of the scientists who seek to trace the origin of the plants found in the Devonian Period, we need to remind ourselves that they seek fossil evidence that will reveal all the grades involved in their theory of the progressive development from the most primitive types discovered to the "well organised" forest types. But the fossil evidence has by no means assisted their theory.

Now scientific men are never afraid of difficulties, and so it is interesting to read the discussions they have upon these difficulties.(58A)

Some writers speak of "rapid transitions", and "discontinuity", and one says: "The cases of sudden changes are by no means rare."

Another viewpoint (58A) is expressed as follows:

"Zeiller's belief that discontinuity is shown, whatever the rank of the groups examined, involves the suggestion of a sudden origin of families or classes, a change altogether without analogy in the present order of things."

Again, the same authority actually gives this advice:

"The only safe assumption appears to be this: that discontinuity proves nothing except our ignorance. There are gaps in the record which no conceivable saltation could have bridged, and thus the supposed explanation leaves us in the lurch just where our difficulty is greatest."

The author then quotes Darwin as follows:

"There are, however, some who still think that species have suddenly given birth, through quite unexplained means, to new and totally different forms . . . but little advantage is gained by believing that new forms are suddenly developed . . . over the old belief in the *creation* of species from the dust of the earth."

DROUGHT-RESISTING SEAWEEDS?

We see that the scientist has very little with which to answer the positive statements in the Bible that God created plants "after their kind" and "whose seed is in itself". He can only parade some of the difficulties which plants would encounter if they proceeded from the sea to evolve on land. We are then informed—because of the factual forest conditions which are observed in the rock record—that by the Devonian Period all the theoretical evolutionary difficulties were overcome, evidently by some pioneer warriors which did not "dry up", but achieved the apparently impossible by developing a specialised system of early drought-resisting roots, which sought nourishment, and a transport system which conveyed that nourishment to all parts of the body of the plant! Truly "there were giants in those days" in the plant world, but unfortunately for evolutionists the records do not display the fossils of the processes to support the theory.

Unrelated theoretical "travelling companions which took the same road" can hardly be exhibited as a proof of an evolutionary process. The admission of "ignorance" because of "discontinuity" and the "gaps" in the records of the early plants, reveals the extreme weakness of the theory. This is surely a concession by these writers to the possibility of their creation. The absence of such evidence from the fossils certainly adds weight to the Biblical presentation.

THE VEGETATION OF THE CARBONIFEROUS ERA

THE HOME—COAL SUPPLY ASSURED

We noticed that the Great Architect worked to a plan. That plan had for its objective the placing upon this earth-sphere men, who, being made in His image and likeness, could be free to exploit all the material resources placed at their disposal.

During the Carboniferous and early Permian Periods we see one of the outstanding features of creative design. In the first place it was a time of most luxuriant vegetation. We are informed that the vegetation attained to forest proportions. The trees were not the usual types found in our forests today. The climatic conditions under which the coal forests grew were warm, swampy, humid conditions,(60) which assisted almost continuous growth. There was NOT the seasonal break which we see today in the summer growth and winter rest.

The nineteenth century could be called the Era for the Development of Coal as a source of power and fuel. In the twentieth century we are finding how indispensable it is. In the coal brought up from the buried layers of the past we have the heat of ancient times which has been stored up for us in a concentrated form. Some scientific men say that they cannot be sure of the exact processes required for its manufacture,(61) but there are some things of which they are certain, and it is interesting for us to note them.

Luxuriant Forests Produced Coal

In the first place the luxuriant forests of this period provided the basic material for the coal beds. It was also a period of volcanic activity,(62) and the carbon dioxide necessary for plants and coal was provided. We are informed that one huge forest would grow, fall into the swampy ground and then descend into a lower position. In the process of time another forest took its place, and fell as had the previous one. In the mines of South Wales as many as 18 layers of coal (layers from 8 feet to 10 feet thick) can be seen. These 18 layers, however, are contained in a thickness of material which would measure something like 8,000 feet, and yet in this enormous thickness of strata the actual coal seams do not make a total of more than about 120 feet in all.(63)

The Magnificent Manufacturer

The picture revealed in the growth of these layers is interesting. We can imagine one layer of vegetation growing up and becoming buried in the debris of sand and grit, then another, and yet another, until there were 18 layers of coal. During the deposition of these layers a giant lowering movement had been going on throughout the areas, wherever the coal beds were being formed.(64) This had been arranged by the Great Architect Himself. Some scientific men think that heat may have been one of the causes of the earth movements, the changes in level possibly resulting from expansion under heat and contraction from cold.(65)

It is interesting to note here what another authority had to say upon this matter:(65A)

"The physical conditions had to be just right for the development
of the coal swamps;

For the growth of the plants whose cellulose was to make up the
coal;

For the subsequent burial of the ancient bogs;

For the growth of folded mountains out of the geo-synclinal area;

And for the preservation of the synclinal coal-bearing folds, from the
200,000,000 years of erosion, since the mountains were formed!

This is a lot to ask of Nature—and a great deal to receive!"

WORLD-WIDE DEPOSITS OF COAL

Last of all, we should note that most of the great continents
have their own coal deposits. However, we must not imagine
that all coal belonged to the one period, though much of the best
and most valuable coal is said to come from the Carboniferous
times.

In the United States the coalfields of this age occupy close to
250,000 square miles,(66) while some Welsh coal seams have
been traced over an area of 1,000 square miles.(67)

To enable us to observe more carefully the design of the
Architect, let me summarise some of the processes which were
necessary for the manufacture of this most essential material for
modern man's needs:

1. There had to be luxuriant vegetation to supply the basic
   material for coal.
2. The coal was manufactured in the area where it grew.
3. A movement that would depress the coalfield was then
   necessary. Eighteen such movements were noted in one
   place alone.
4. These downward movements of the earth had to be arranged
   for regular periods which would synchronise with matured
   growth of vegetation in each layer.
5. Great pressures upon this primary material were necessary.
6. So that the various continents upon which man was to dwell
   would have coal supplies, the growth of the material and the
   depressing movements had to be very extensive.

A summary such as this helps us to see the logic in the scripture
presentation. Design calls for a Designer, just as a complex
building calls for a skilled Architect. The more intricate and

complicated the design, the more wisdom is needed from the Designer. It follows, then, that the tremendous amount of very complicated design expressed in creation calls for a Tremendous Creative Intelligence.

BIBLIOGRAPHY

51. *Earth Lore*, p. 17, S. J. Shand. **52.** Ref. as (51), p. 18. **53.** *The Building of Australia and the Succession of Life*, part i, p. 103, Prof. W. Howchin, 1930. **53A.** *The Succession of Life Through Geological Time*, pp. 10, 13, British Museum (Natural History). **54.** Ref. as (53), p. 47. **55.** *Luther Burbank*, vol. ii, p. 232. **56.** *The Science of Life*, vol. ii, p. 483, Wells and Huxley. **57.** Ref. as (56), p. 472. **58.** Ref. as (56), p. 473. **58A.** *Extinct Plants and the Problems of Evolution*, p. 220, D. H. Scott. **59.** Ref. as (56), p. 483. **59A.** *The Evolution of Plants*, p. 221, D. H. Scott. **60.** *Coal and Its Story*, p. 136, E. A. Martin. **61.** Ref. as (60), p. 111. **62.** Ref. as (60), p. 168. **63.** Ref. as (60), pp. 140, 157. **64.** Ref. as (60), p. 158. **65.** Ref. as (60), p. 166. **65A.** *Down to Earth*, p. 353, Croneis and Krumbein. **66.** Ref. as (65A), p. 352. **67.** Ref. as (53A), p. 26.

THE FOURTH ERA:
THE CLEARING OF THE ATMOSPHERE

The Sacred Record—Genesis 1: 14–19

"And God said:

Let there be lights in the expanse of the heaven, to divide the day from the night;

And let them be for signs, and for seasons, and for days, and years;

And let there be lights in the expanse of the heaven to give light upon the earth: and it was so.

And God appointed the two great lights; the greater light to dominate the day, and the lesser light to dominate the night and the stars.

And God set them in the expanse of the heaven to give light upon the earth, and to dominate the day and the night, and to divide the light from the darkness: and God saw that it was good.

And there was evening and there was morning, the Fourth Day."

CORRELATION OF GEOLOGICAL MATERIAL WITH
THE SCRIPTURE RECORDS

GEOLOGICAL *RECORD*			*SCRIPTURE* *RECORD*

Modern flowering plants arrive in great profusion	Mesozoic Era	Cretaceous	
New life of Mesozoic Era Permanent seasons noted		Jurassic	God appointed TWO great lights —to dominate the day and night (Gen. 1: 16)
		Triassic	Let the lights in the expanse (atmosphere) (*a*) divide day from night; (*b*) be for signs and seasons; (*c*) days and years
Inland seas dry up, leaving large deposits of salt Desert conditions in northern hemisphere and glacial conditions in southern hemisphere at about same time **Great climatic changes noted**		Permian Period	*Note:* In the Carboniferous and Permian Periods, though sufficient light came through the atmosphere from the sun for the growth of abundant vegetation, yet the sun did *not dominate* in the expanse or atmosphere as it did in the later Mesozoic Era.
Wet humid conditions		Carboniferous Period	

Read upwards ↑

94

THE FOURTH ERA:
THE CLEARING OF THE ATMOSPHERE

 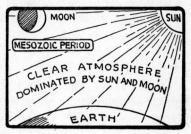

One suggestion of the change in the atmosphere between the Carboniferous Period and Mesozoic Era.

> "And God appointed two great lights, the greater for the rule [domination] of the day and the lesser for the rule [domination] of the night" (Gen. 1:16).

THE HOME—THE LIGHTING SYSTEM MODERNISED

Unfortunately there has been some confusion over the interpretation of the work of the Creator in the Fourth "Day" or Era. The confusion is unfortunate but easily understood when the facts are known. We must again remember that *the Bible story* was written about 3,500 years ago in Hebrew. The science of geology is only about 150 years old, and the English translators of the Bible in 1611 did not have any scientific facts to guide their minds when translating from the Hebrew to the English.

Let me illustrate this point by taking verse 21 of Genesis 1. "God created great whales" is the reading of the Authorised Version (1611). The Hebrew word, however, does not specify "whales" but sea or land "monsters" (Hebrew *Tanniynim*), and when translated literally reads: "God created great monsters."

It is readily accepted by all geologists that the great monsters or reptiles were the outstanding feature of the era prior to mammals and man. When translating in 1611, "a whale" was the biggest "monster" then known, and this wrong interpretation of the sea monsters was given, and under the circumstances could not be easily corrected. It is these incorrect presentations of the Creator's work that make modern scientific men turn from the Bible narrative, for they give not only an unscientific idea but also suggest a wrong order in the creation of life by naming a whale (mammal) as arriving with the first flying things and reptiles.

THE HEBREW EXACTNESS

Today as we closely check the language used by the Hebrew writer we find that his statements fit perfectly with the discovered facts. The English Authorised translation of this story of Creation is not quite exact enough when placed alongside a scientific investigation of the fossil facts. As we go back to the literal Hebrew we get the perfect picture conveyed to Moses that the Holy Spirit intended us to have.

In the past, as men read the Authorised English translation (1611) of the Creation story, they very naturally but erroneously *thought* that the work of God in the Fourth "Day" referred to the *creation* of the sun and moon. We now see from the Hebrew, as well as from the geological records, that this interpretation was wrong, for several reasons:

1. The Hebrew words used in verse 16 and translated "made" (Hebrew 'Asah) does *not mean "to create"* but one of its meanings is "to appoint". We now understand that the work of God on the Fourth "Day" was giving a new appointment to the sun and moon. Henceforth they were appointed to "dominate" or "rule" in the atmosphere. They had *not so dominated in the previous (Carboniferous) Period.*

2. We have already noticed in verses 4 and 5 that in the First "Day" God "divided between the light and between the darkness". *The sun was in its place in the heavens from "the beginning" of the First "Day"*, as maintained by astronomers and geologists and as indicated by the Genesis writer in verses 4 and 5.

3. Yet another fact assists us. We have already surveyed the

work of the Creator in the Third "Day"—the era of very luxuriant vegetation, when light and heat from the sun was necessary to enable the vegetation to grow rapidly. We know that without the sun's light and warmth plant life could not exist. But we now learn that in this era of luxuriant vegetation the sun, though present in the heavens, did NOT "dominate" or "rule" in the atmosphere. The conditions required for the rapid, uninterrupted growth of vegetation were humid, cloudy, swampy conditions, with plenty of carbon dioxide in the atmosphere. When God saw that the world had a large supply of coal He altered the conditions, and an altogether new era—noted in both sacred and scientific records—dawned.

4. There is a further important point to be noted. Verse 14 in the Authorised Version now reads:

"And God said, '*Let there be lights* in the firmament of the heaven to divide the day from the night.'"

But from the Hebrew text it would be just as correct to render this as follows:

"And God said, '*Let the lights which are* in the firmament of the heaven divide the day from the night.'"

There is a great difference in our understanding of these two renderings. As it stands at present, the Authorised translation, which reads "Let there be lights", implies that there were NO LIGHTS in the firmament at that time and therefore God placed them there in that day.

The Hebrew text, however, can be read to imply that the lights were ALREADY IN THEIR POSITION AT THAT TIME—"Let the lights (which are) in the heavens" —and that God was merely giving them a NEW APPOINTMENT. This latter rendering of the Hebrew would therefore agree with the scientific facts noted by the geologists in the tremendous climatic changes observed towards the close of the Palaeozoic Era and the beginning of the new era known as the Mesozoic, when great monsters and flying things arrived.

G

The moon is God's great monthly calendar used by early man and Eastern peoples.

LIGHTS APPOINTED TO DOMINATE

The words used in the Scripture give us the key to the discovered scientific facts. God's Word says that God appointed two great lights to "dominate" or "rule" where previously they had *not* done so.

The Tables A and D mark the position of the great climatic changes that took place on the earth towards the close of the Permian Period. There was a glacial period which, according to the Australian geologist Sir Douglas Mawson, lasted about 25 million years. The old, humid, swampy and, according to some writers, most likely cloudy conditions finished. The Permian Period brought to an end the long era known in geology as the Palaeozoic.

As a result of this complete domination of the sun in the expanse, altogether new conditions became evident, and these are reflected in the layers and fossils of the geological record. The geologist notes desert conditions in Europe where previously the sea had spread over the land and swampy conditions had prevailed. The dominating sun dried up the inland water both in America and Europe, and in America left behind huge deposits of salt estimated to be about 30 million million tons.(70) The great climatic changes, noted as a result of this new appointment, also made possible tremendous advances in the plant and animal life of the earth, as we shall see later.

DRASTIC CHANGES NOTED

Several quotations chosen from many similar are worth recording here.(71) One authority says:

"Physical changes took place over much of the earth's surface towards the close of the Carboniferous Period and extended over most of the Permo-Carboniferous Period, which created a crisis in the vegetable world. . . . Something happened . . . by which this cosmopolitan flora came to a relatively sudden end . . . and its place was taken by other plants which gave a new facies to the vegetable world. What led to such a sweeping change in plant life at that time is not definitely known, but there is a high probability that it was caused by important modifications in the physical conditions of the earth's surface, especially in relation to climate."

An English Geologist writes as follows:(72)

"The drastic changes in environment during the Permian appear to have allowed only those animals which could adapt themselves to new conditions to survive."

Again, speaking of the new Triassic Period:(72)

"The continents consisted largely of deserts . . . plains occupied by shifting sand-dunes; delta fans, formed by seasonal torrents; and temporary lakes and salt pools . . . the prevailing red colour of the sandstones and marls of the Trias . . . indicates that hot and dry conditions prevailed on most lands."

Let us take hold of the vital facts mentioned and summarise them in the words expressed by these scientific investigators.

OUR FIRST AUTHORITY (71) NOTES:

1. Physical changes took place
2. over much of the earth's surface.
3. They occurred at the close of the Carboniferous period
4. and created a crisis in the vegetable world (of that period).
5. The flora came to a relatively sudden end
6. and was replaced by other plants.
7. The cause of the sweeping change
8. is not definitely known to the scientists.
9. It is suggested as a high probability
10. that it was caused by important modifications in the physical conditions of the earth's surface,
11. particularly in relation to climate.

THE SECOND AUTHORITY (72) noted:

12. Drastic changes
13. in the Permian period.
14. Only certain animals survived
15. which adapted themselves to the new conditions.
16. In the next period (Triassic)
17. continents now consist largely of deserts,
18. shifting sand dunes, temporary lakes,
19. and salt pools.
20. Hot and dry conditions now prevailed in most lands.

All these details make a fascinating and interesting commentary upon the changed conditions noted by geologists, and they emphasize more than any words of mine some of the things that happened on the earth after God gave His new appointment to the sun.

 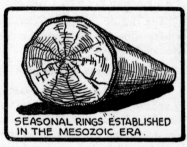

The great climatic change between the Palaeozoic and Mesozoic Eras is reflected in the changes of vegetation and animals.

THE UNIVERSAL CALENDAR

Because of the tremendous changes that took place in the record of the rocks a new era has been noted by the geologist and called the Mesozoic. It is therefore to be expected that the Genesis writer should also note the importance of this new aspect of the Creator's work by placing it in another "day" or era.

For the first time in the sacred record "seasons" are mentioned. From the Mesozoic Era the geologists find seasons permanently established and new types of trees becoming features in it. The seasonal rings, which became permanent features in the new vegetation, and the arrival of altogether new types of living things bear testimony to the tremendous climatic changes noted at this time for which no satisfactory scientific explanation has been given.

Speaking of the New Period (Jurassic) one writer remarks:(73)

"Conditions on the land were generally temperate and the rainfall sufficient to support a luxuriant vegetation. Although growth rings in some Jurassic trees indicate locally well-marked seasons, the climate was prevailingly mild."

THE MOON APPOINTED FOR SEASONS

The Psalmist says: "He appointed the moon for seasons" (Ps. 104: 19). We little realise, in these days of calendars, the prominent place the moon had in the lives of the ancients. Eastern people have always regulated their fasts, feasts and seasons by it. Even today the Moslem world observes Ramadan from the first appearance of the moon in a particular month. As this season of fasting approaches, the appearance of the new moon is most anxiously awaited, and when first sighted in Europe the news is flashed to Egypt and other Moslem countries, so that preparations can be made.

The Jewish seasons of the Passover, Pentecost, etc., are still timed by the lunar calendar. We need to be reminded perhaps that our English word "month" comes from an Anglo-Saxon word meaning "moon".

PALAEOZOIC ERA CLOSES WITH CLIMATIC CHANGES

The essential thing for us to keep in mind, however, is that the sacred writer in his anticipation of modern geological discoveries testifies that a new era, in which the sun received a new appointment and dominated the atmosphere, occurred *after* the introduction of vegetation and *before* the era of great monsters. (See Table A.)

Throughout the world the rock records bear witness to the tremendous climatic changes that took place at the close of the Palaeozoic Era; and after a long devastating glacial period the sun so emerged as a dominating factor in the atmosphere that desert conditions prevailed, dried up inland seas, leaving huge salt deposits, and when seasons became established, new types of vegetation displayed seasonal rings henceforth.

SUMMARY

In order to impress our minds with the value of the evidence reviewed in this era, perhaps it would be worth while summarising the general facts which refer to the climatic changes due to the domination of the sun that began in the Permian Period.

1. The swampy humid conditions of the Carboniferous Period ceased.
2. A long glacial period has been noted in the southern hemisphere.
3. This was succeeded in many lands by dry desert conditions.
4. Inland seas also dried up in Europe and America.
5. Huge salt deposits amounting to millions of tons resulted in the Mesozoic Era from this new dry condition.
6. Many types of vegetation belonging to the Palaeozoic Era ceased.
7. New types of vegetation dominated the land.
8. Seasonal growth in trees became a permanent feature from the new era.
9. New types of animal life dominated the sea, land and air.
10. The next big feature in the New Era revealed great numbers of reptilian monsters in possession of the earth and its waters.
11. The results of the climatic changes were so marked that geologists made a new era called the Mesozoic.

If the Biblical presentation has been misunderstood in the past because of our ignorance of the geological evidence, there is now no excuse for this. The sacred writer has isolated his details under the heading of another "day", and we cannot fail to notice that those details have been placed in the correct scientific order.

BIBLIOGRAPHY

70. *Down to Earth*, p. 356, Croneis and Krumbein, 1946. **71.** *The Building of Australia*, part i, p. 174, Prof. W. Howchin. **72.** *The Succession of Life Through Geological Times*, pp. 28, 31, British Museum. **73.** Ref. as (72), p. 34.

TABLE E

CORRELATION OF GEOLOGICAL MATERIAL WITH THE SCRIPTURE RECORDS

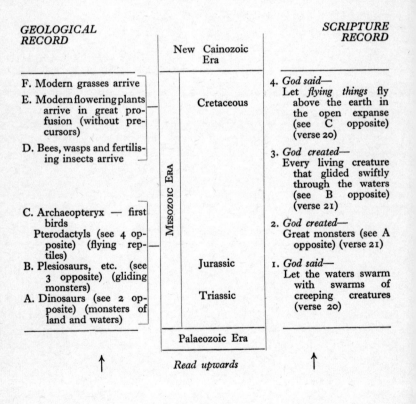

GEOLOGICAL RECORD

New Cainozoic Era

SCRIPTURE RECORD

F. Modern grasses arrive
E. Modern flowering plants arrive in great profusion (without precursors)
D. Bees, wasps and fertilising insects arrive

Cretaceous

4. *God said—*
   Let *flying things* fly above the earth in the open expanse (see C opposite) (verse 20)

3. *God created—*
   Every living creature that glided swiftly through the waters (see B opposite) (verse 21)

C. Archaeopteryx — first birds
   Pterodactyls (see 4 opposite) (flying reptiles)
B. Plesiosaurs, etc. (see 3 opposite) (gliding monsters)
A. Dinosaurs (see 2 opposite) (monsters of land and waters)

MESOZOIC ERA

Jurassic

Triassic

2. *God created—*
   Great monsters (see A opposite) (verse 21)

1. *God said—*
   Let the waters swarm with swarms of creeping creatures (verse 20)

Palaeozoic Era

↑

Read upwards

↑

THE FIFTH ERA:
GREAT MONSTERS AND MODERN PLANTS

The Sacred Record: Genesis 1 : 20–3

"AND GOD SAID:

Let the waters swarm with swarms of living creatures that hath
  soul,
And let winged things wing, above the earth in the open ex-
  panse of heaven.
And God created the great monsters,
And every living creature that glided swiftly,
With which the waters swarmed after their kind, and every
  winged thing after his kind:
And God saw that it was good.
And God blessed them, saying, Be fruitful, and multiply, and
  fill the waters in the seas, and let winged things multiply
  in the earth.
And there was evening and there was morning, the Fifth Day."

THE FIFTH ERA:
GREAT MONSTERS AND MODERN PLANTS

Monsters of the Mesozoic Era.

"God said, Let the waters swarm with swarms of living creatures that hath soul" (Gen. 1: 20).

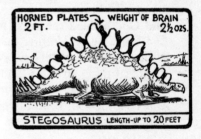

THE SPACIOUS GROUNDS—NEW OCCUPANTS IN POSSESSION

With the complete domination of the sun in the atmosphere, further interesting results are seen in the great variety of new life that the fossil records of the Mesozoic Era have preserved for us, but first of all let us observe the literal Hebrew text.

In the phrase quoted above, the Hebrew word *Sharats*, translated "bring forth abundantly", literally means "swarm with swarms". This expression is also used in the Bible referring to the plagues at the time of the exodus of the children of Israel from Egypt. On that occasion frogs "swarmed" everywhere—in the fields, houses, beds, and even interfered with the making of bread (see Exod. 9: 3).

REPTILES IN POSSESSION

Keeping in mind the sacred writer's introductory description of the life of this new era, it is very interesting to observe Professor Howchin's summary concerning the life that now appeared. He says:(75)

"The reptilia greatly increased in numbers, specialisation and physical form. They took possession of the land, the fresh waters, the sea, and the air, and attained a maximum development for the race which made the Mesozoic Era."

He also writes:(76)

"In passing from the Permian to the Mesozoic, we are conscious of entering a new world in the succession of life. The change did not occur by a cataclysm or sudden ending of the old order of things, but followed as incidental to a slow change in the physical conditions of life over large areas of the earth's surface. . . . A whole volume of records is missing. When we next gather up the threads of the story we find that the organic world had made extraordinary advances during the age *of which we have no available records.*"

Professor Howchin's remarks have been selected here because they are representative of the facts which have also been observed by other leading palaeontologists and geologists concerning the tremendous changes noted at the close of the Permian Period.

Could we have a better testimony to the accuracy of the facts as expressed by the sacred writer? When the scientific specialist parades his evidence he sees no sign of a cataclysm in the geological layers. There was no "sudden ending of the older order of things". However, new layers and their fossil contents make him not only conscious that he is entering a *new world* in the succession of life but, to use Howchin's own phrase, "this new life took possession of the land, freshwaters, sea and air". What a delightful commentary this makes upon the Genesis text: "Let the waters swarm with swarms!" Of course, to one who holds the theory of the gradual evolution of life it would certainly appear that "a whole volume of the records is missing".

The *creation of new life* as maintained in the Genesis story seems to have the habit of leaving big gaps in the geological

records, only to those who are looking for material evidence to
support their theory of evolution.

The scientific exactness of the literal Hebrew describing these sea and
land monsters is challenging.

"And God created the great
monsters and all living soul
that glided swiftly, with which
the waters swarmed, after their
kind" (Gen. 1: 21).

GREAT MONSTERS HAVE THEIR DAY

Next in order both in the rock and sacred records come the
great monsters, flying things, and swiftly moving creatures of
the sea. As I have mentioned previously, it is important to
follow the correct translation as shown above.

Scientists who have studied the fossil remains of the great
monsters of this new era are most eloquent in their descriptions
of these enormous beasts. They are known as Dinosaurs, meaning
"Terrible Lizards".(77) There was a great variety of these
animals, and their lengths, heights and weights differed greatly,
though weights of 30 to 40 tons are mentioned.(78)

The largest of them, called Diplodocus, has the reputation of
being the longest animal which ever walked on land, for it was
85 feet from the tip of its tail to its head, and stood about 16
feet high. Another fearsome-looking creature named Bronto-
saurus or "Thunder Lizard" was about 65 feet long.(79) Both
these animals lived on plants and no doubt spent a great amount
of time in the water, because the water helped to support the

weight of their enormous bodies. Another peculiar feature of these "monsters" was that, although their bodies were so tremendous, their heads were small and their brains even smaller than we would imagine, for in many cases they weighed only a few pounds, and in other cases only a few ounces.(80)

There were many types of these land reptiles. Some evidently fought with each other, for it is noted from their mouths, teeth and huge claws that they were possibly flesh-eating animals. Tyrannosaurus must have looked a rather fearsome creature; its length was something like 47 feet and its height 20 feet.(81) Brachiosaurus stood about 30 feet high and had a length of about 60 feet, and is said to have weighed about 50 tons. Another was known as Allosaurus or "The Leaping Lizard". In Belgium in 1872 some miners came across about twenty-two complete skeletons of another type known as Iguanodon.(82) Each of these could have stood to a height of 30 feet. Then there was the Triceratops, a beast about 25 feet long with a skull 6 feet across, embellished with three horns.(83) A few years ago an American expedition found a nest of fossilised eggs, each about 6 inches in length, in the Gobi desert.(84) Although the Stegosaurus was another fearsome-looking creature, it was a vegetarian and, we are told, one of the gentlest of dinosaurs.(85) However, if its disposition were "gentle", its appearance was otherwise. Its 30-foot armoured form carried a series of large, upstanding, flat bones, each about 30 inches high, and on its tail four large spikes. We are informed that although it possibly weighed as much as 10 tons, its brain was fantastically small, no larger than that of a kitten.

One could go on for some time describing these creatures with their peculiarities, for they were many, but once again we note that the geologist has provided us with another picturesque commentary upon the words of the ancient writer: "God created great monsters."

THE SWIFTLY GLIDING SEA-MONSTERS

The Genesis writer, however, now introduces us to something vastly different from the ponderous, slow-moving monsters which crept upon the land and lived in the shallow waters. He speaks further of creatures that "moveth, which the waters brought forth abundantly". The Hebrew word for "moveth" is *ramas* and it means "to move lightly", "to glide about", "to glide swiftly". The word for "brought forth abundantly" conveys the idea of "to swarm" or "to teem", so that we may translate:

"And God created great monsters *and every swiftly gliding living creature* with which the waters swarmed."

Again we find that the description given is by no means accidental. The scientists picture such enormous sea creatures as Mosasaurus, Plesiosaurus, and Ichthyosaurus,(86) all of which attained great lengths and had one special feature, a very rapid seal-like movement through the waters. About 100 different kinds of Plesiosaurs have been found in various parts of the world, differing in length from 3 feet to 40 feet.(87) Many fossil Ichthyosaurs have also been found. These moved through the waters more by means of a flexible tail than the use of their "paddles". As many as seven fossilised babies were found in the skeleton of a mother Ichthyosaurus, showing that their young were born alive as are baby whales.(88)

Dr. Herbert Ryle, Dean of Westminster (1914), when writing about the words used by the writer of Genesis, said:

"The Hebrew word translated 'moveth' denotes a gliding swift movement of the fish for which there is no adequate English equivalent." (89)

FLYING THINGS ARE INTRODUCED

It is interesting for us to notice first that the word "fowl", as used by the early translators, does not do justice either to the Hebrew text or to the other creatures created in this era. Among the animals discovered we find a great many did NOT possess feathers, but had wings of skin something like bats. These peculiar flying things were called by the scientists Pterodactyls, which means "Wing Finger", so-called because of the fingers on each wing.(90) These creatures were not birds but *flying reptiles*, some of which measured up to 25 feet across the wings.

However, the first created birds also belong to this era. The complete skeleton of one, known as Archaeopteryx, or "Ancient Wing", has been discovered.(91) From their claws and teeth it

Monsters of the air and sea.

"And God said . . . Let flying things fly above the earth in the open expanse of heaven" (Gen. 1: 20).

is thought that this kind may have lived on fish. It is said to have been a little smaller than a crow and to have had a long tail, the feathers of which spread out like a fan.

Notice particularly that the sacred writer did not say "Let *birds* fly" but rather "Let flying things fly". It is true that birds did fly in this era, and this statement if used would have been correct but not complete. It was necessary to use words which would *include other flying creatures* besides birds, such as, for example, the Pterodactyls (flying reptiles).

SCIENCE ANTICIPATED BY SCRIPTURE

The Hebrew of the sacred record has carefully and delightfully anticipated the modern scientists' findings by over 3,000 years. It does seem as though God is giving scientific proof to a scientific age, so that men will know with certainty that this is His own record.

Having looked at the varied and peculiar life of the new era, which, as the Genesis writer informed us, was created "after its kind", it is rather fascinating for us to summarise the details again and place them alongside the facts paraded in all text-books on geology and palaeontology.

The Bible Description	The Scientific Description
1. God created great (sea or land) monsters (verse 21).	1. Fossil remains of huge monsters such as Dinosaurs, Diplodocus, Tyrannosaurs, Iguanodon, Triceratops, Brachiosaurs, Stegosaurs, etc.
2. Their habitat was "in the waters" (verses 20 and 21).	2. "They took possession of the freshwaters and sea" (Howchin).
3. Many monsters of the sea had "a swift gliding movement" (Hebrew) (verse 21).	3. Fossil remains of such swiftly moving marine creatures as Ichthyosaurus, Plesiosaurus, Mosasaurus.
4. They "swarmed with swarms" (Hebrew) (verses 20 and 21).	4. "They took possession of the land, freshwater, sea and air" (Howchin).
5. "Let winged things fly" (Hebrew) (verse 20).	5. Fossil remains of *birds* and *winged reptiles* such as Pterodactyls, Archaeopteryx, Pteranodons, have been found.

It is also interesting to note that Dr. W. Bennett says(91A) that the Hebrew word Tanniynim, translated "monsters", can be explained as "a stretched-out, long, thin thing, like a serpent".

Such a parade of outstanding geological material has provided every student with another unsuspected and very delightful scientific commentary upon the Genesis narrative. This gives an added thrill, because it is realised only too well that for years all we have been given to digest has been the usual theological hash about "Babylonian myths". Now we have been awakened to find that the words of the Hebrew text have turned out to be scientifically correct in every detail. Their exactness carries a tremendous challenge to every thoughtful reader.

THE CREATION OF MODERN PLANTS AND GRASSES

Plants of Great Beauty Arrive

It is interesting and important to point out here that while new forms of animal life were appearing other forms continued in existence. But plant life, too, has its own story. Certain forms of plants continued their existence while others came into being. It is at this point in the story, towards the end of the era of great monsters, that an amazing event took place in the story of plants.

In the geological strata of the Cretaceous Period which is the last period of the Mesozoic Era, there arrived entirely new types of plant life. We cannot pass over this without observing some very interesting facts. The modern flowering plants, known to the botanist as angiosperms, first appear in this period. These plants arrived in great abundance, with grasses, cereals, a great variety of shrubs which bore seeds and fruit, along with many modern types of vegetation.

The Sudden Invasion by Modern Plants

Professor W. B. Scott remarks upon the "extreme suddenness of the invasion which swept over the earth" and then goes on to speak of "the completeness of the revolution of the flora", of which, he says, "there can be no question".(92) In the earliest rocks of the Mesozoic Era the botanists and geologists find only certain well-established types of vegetation, such as ferns, cycads, ginkgoes and conifers,(93) but in the later rocks of this era they discover new plants in great profusion. One writer says that 90 per cent of these were kinds known to us today.(94) We can well understand their surprise. Have they not acclaimed a theory of evolution which, according to one accepted authority, required(95)

"gradual development from the simple inorganic condition of primal matter to the complex structure of the physical universe"?

and also accepted the theory of

"a gradual unfolding and branching out into all the varied forms of beings which constitute the animal and plant kingdoms"?

H

FOSSIL FACTS ARE STUBBORN THINGS

It would seem as though the fossils of the modern plants discovered by scientists did not behave themselves. As a cricketer would say, "The beggars did not play the game." Instead of dropping fully developed into the Cretaceous layers so suddenly, they should have started to show themselves ages back in the Devonian, or even in the Carboniferous, or, even if when they arrived they had been a little more primitive in form, then the scientists would not have worried so much, for that is what they had proclaimed in their theory, but to arrive in great abundance as highly specialised things of beauty, as modern plants are, seems to have caused great vexation of spirit to thinking evolutionists.

But facts concerning the fossils of the Cretaceous Period have played a worse trick on the scientists! Bees, wasps and other insects, which were necessary for the fertilising of the modern flowers, arrived in the same era as the plants and their flowers.(97) The creationists really have the laugh on the evolutionists. Why bees, wasps and other insects necessary for the pollination of flowers should arrive without giving some kind of warning is incomprehensible to evolutionists because it advertises design and a designer. To make the evolutionist satisfied these well-organised honey-gatherers andtheir friends should have left some primitive fossilised ancestors in earlier layers, so that every step or mutation in the unfolding process could be observed by us today.

FOOD ARRIVED BEFORE ANIMALS

There are other facts, however, which should add to the confusion of the evolutionists. They observe that land mammals have arrived by the next era (known as the Cainozoic) and discover that the grasses and cereals upon which these beasts were to live and thrive arrived in the geological period *before* the animals.(98) The creationists see in all this the well-thought-out plan of an All-wise Creator. Naturally it would be useless to create or evolve animals *before* their food, but quite logical for food (grasses) to be created before the animals, as happened in the case under review. The bees, wasps and other fertilising insects give the same testimony, and proclaim it as loudly as their fossil remains can. It was arranged by the Great Designer and Architect that these creatures should arrive with the flowers upon which they were to work. One without the other would be practically useless.

Notice how easily one writer passes over the difficulties caused by the *suddenness and abundance of the arrival* of these plants and their allies in his statement of the facts:

"In the earlier part of the Cretaceous Period . . . the vegetation on the lowlands was similar to that of the Jurassic; cycads, conifers and ferns were the dominant types of plant life. By the middle of the period the higher flowering plants or angiosperms had appeared, and in later Cretaceous times the vegetation almost everywhere was essentially of a modern type. It included shrubs and deciduous trees strikingly similar to the living fig, magnolia, poplar and plane. The extremely rapid rise of the angiosperms has not yet been fully explained. The mutual adaptation of pollinating insects and honey-bearing flowers may have been an important factor in their success."(99)

However, we lose sight of an important point if we under-value the scientists' own testimony as to the "extremely rapid rise" of these new major types of life. Professors Dana and Raymond noted this suddenness in the arrival of the invertebrate marine animals in the Cambrian waters, and almost every text-book on geology makes some comment upon the fact. Wells and Huxley saw it in the land vegetation that arrived as "travelling companions", and which became well-established forests in the Devonian, without *precursors*. Professor Howchin and others have noted the same suddenness in the arrival of great monsters in the waters and flying things in the air.

TRUTH AND BEAUTY DWELL TOGETHER

It will be well at this point to quote another well-known authority who has commented at some length upon the sudden arrival of the modern types of plants in the Cretaceous Period in these words:(100)

"The apparently sudden appearance of quite well-developed flowering plants is still perhaps the greatest difficulty in the record of evolution. The angiosperms must have had a previous history of some kind and must, we may assume, have been derived from some older group of plants."

"They seem to burst forth in full panoply and without ancestors in the upper Cretaceous."

Again he says:(**100A**)

"The whole problem of descent is, in fact, extraordinarily complex. . . . Evolution, during the periods to which our records extend, proves to have been by no means a regular advance from the simple to the complex. Very often, indeed, the reverse has been the case."

The following quotation from the same authority is, perhaps, just as interesting and perhaps surprising:(**101**)

"Darwin writing in 1879 to Sir Joseph Hooker said, 'The rapid development so far as we can judge of all the higher plants within recent geological times is an abominable mystery.'"

As we have already seen, the matter of this abrupt appearance of new forms of life throughout the geological ages has caused serious questioning on the part of many research workers, both in England and elsewhere. Here is yet another quotation from the pen of a leading French professor to whom was entrusted the task of writing one volume of a series of twelve, in which he had to summarise the available material relating to the earth and its life before history began. As his professional mind studied the available facts, in fairness to the truth, he realised the point that is being made in this book. It makes the student of the Bible feel that when all evidence about the facts and fossils is paraded without prejudice, it merely serves as a very detailed and powerful commentary on the scientific accuracy of the Genesis record. This is what he says:(**102**)

"The comparatively abrupt appearance of so many organic forms has sometimes been regarded as evidence against the evolutionary theory. Again and again it has been proved that a new flora and fauna have suddenly appeared in some geological stratum after the complete disappearance of older ones preserved in the strata immediately antecedent, and the most ardent disciples of Cuvier considered this an unanswerable argument in favour of the hypothesis of independent creations."

Statements such as these should be weighed well by all readers. These opinions have not been written by unbalanced, emotional,

or irresponsible persons. They are from the generally accepted
authorities in their branch of research. Text-books of botany
and geology do not dispute the problem caused by the multitude
of missing precursors of modern plant life, or the sharp breaks
in the continuity of the typical plants of an older period, and
those of a new(102A) although they usually state that the
"missing links" must at one time have existed, and may yet be
discovered.

MODERN FLOWERS NEED SUNLIGHT

One further thought should be noticed here. We have seen
how the Genesis writer made a special feature of the domination
of the sun in the Fourth "Day" or Era. Here is another fact
in the fossil evidence which supports this statement. Modern
plants, with their varied colours and perfumes, need strong
sunlight. We now see the Wisdom that waited for the cloudy,
swampy, humid conditions of the Carboniferous Period to cease
and the sun's domination to begin, before creating plants with
their sparkling colours and delightful perfumes.

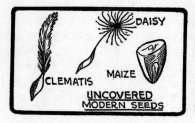

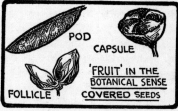

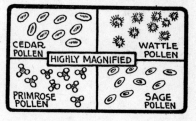

Every flowering plant has its own
peculiar seed and pollen.

The inspired record is so well supported by facts manifesting
creative intelligence of the very highest order as to constitute
the strongest of challenges. On the other hand, the theory of

continuous organic evolution fails at the most critical points when the fossils of new life are found, in new periods, without precursors.

It should be mentioned here as a matter of interest that there is a tendency on the part of some modern thinkers to depart from the original idea of "gradual development" or "gradual unfolding" in the theory of evolution.

SUDDEN ARRIVALS CHANGE A THEORY

As we are noting, the evidence of various geological layers shows instances of "sudden arrivals" of new life, and we must not be surprised when we observe amendments to the old theory being suggested.

BIBLIOGRAPHY

75. *The Building of Australia*, vol. ii, p. 337, Prof. W. Howchin. **76.** Ref. as (75), p. 331. **77.** *Extinct Animals* (Puffin Series), p. 10, Hilary Stebbing. **78.** *Historical Geology*, p. 281, Prof. R. C. Hussey. **79.** *Animals of Yesterday* (University of Chicago Series), pp. 4–5, Bertha Morris Parker. **80.** Ref. as (35), p. 512. **81.** Ref. as (77), p. 31. **82.** Ref. as (77), p. 31. **83.** Ref. as (77), p. 11. **84.** *The Corridor of Life*, p. 165, Swinton and Pinner, 1948. **85.** Ref. as (84), p. 159. **86.** Ref. as (84), pp. 167–77. **87.** Ref. as (77), p. 8. **88.** *Man and the Vertebrates*, p. 116, A. S. Romer. **89.** *Cambridge Bible*, Genesis, p. 15, Dr. Herbert Ryle. **90.** Ref. as (79), pp. 8, 30. **91.** Ref. as (79), pp. 21–2. **91A.** "Genesis" (*The Century Bible*), p. 81, W. H. Bennett. **92.** *An Introduction to Geology*, 3rd. ed., vol. ii, 1932, p. 288, Prof. W. B. Scott, Sc.D., LL.D. **93.** *Extinct Plants and Problems of Evolution*, pp. 59–60, 103–4, D. H. Scott, M.A., LL.D. **94.** Ref. as (92), p. 243, Prof. W. B. Scott, Sc.D., LL.D. **95.** *Organic Evolution*, p. 6, Prof. R. S. Lull, 1940. **97.** *The Evolution of Plants*, p. 42, Dr. D. H. Scott, M.A., LL.D. **98.** *Historical Geology*, p. 505, Prof. R. C. Moore. **99.** *The Succession of Life Through Geological Time*, p. 41, British Museum (Natural History), 1949. **100.** Ref. as (97), p. 40. **100A.** Ref. as (97), p. 237. **101.** Ref. as (97), p. 37. **102.** *The Earth before History*, p. 75, E. Perrier, 1925. **102A.** Ref. as (93), p. 105.

THE SIXTH ERA:
LAND MAMMALS

The Sacred Record: Genesis 1: 24, 28

"AND GOD SAID:

Let the *Earth* bring forth living soul after his kind, cattle and creeping thing, and beast of the earth after his kind: and it was so. And God made the beast of the earth after his kind, and cattle after their kind, and every thing that creepeth upon the earth after his kind; and God saw that it was good."

TABLE F

CORRELATION OF THE GEOLOGICAL MATERIAL WITH THE SCRIPTURE RECORDS

GEOLOGICAL RECORD			SCRIPTURE RECORD
Man appears and dominates the earth		Pleistocene	*And God said—* 4. Let us make man in our image and likeness, and let him have dominion over the earth
	CAINOZOIC ERA	Pliocene	
Beasts of the earth, cattle and other land mammals arrive		Miocene	3. Beasts of the earth 2. Cattle and creeping things
		Oligocene	*God said—*
		Eocene	1. Let the earth bring forth living soul
Modern grasses and plants arrive Era of great monsters ↑		Mesozoic Era *Read upwards*	↑

120

THE SIXTH ERA:
LAND MAMMALS

Some beasts of the earth (mammals) which arrived before man.

"And God made the beast of the earth . . . and cattle . . . and everything that creepeth upon the earth after his kind" (Gen. 1: 25).

PROVISION FOR DOMESTIC SUPPLIES

Again, there is agreement between the records in the Book of the Rocks and the Book of Genesis. Our scientific friends have placed the new era of mammals *after* the reptilian monsters and *before* the arrival of man (see chart). Let us notice some of the specific details that the writers have given us. In this new era both the Rock and the Book records express identical ideas, but naturally different phrasing is used. The sacred writer correctly placed the creation of beasts of the earth and the cattle (mammals) in the same era. The geologist and the Genesis writer have both noted the fact that they arrived after the *era of reptilian monsters* and *prior to man*. The Genesis writer provided descriptive pictures, and the animals are easily recognised. A presentation which had to be passed down thirty-five centuries and translated into many languages needed to be simple and picturesque.

The Biblical writer has also correctly registered other points. In the Fifth "Day" (verse 20) it was "*the waters*" that brought forth their swarms (verse 20), but in the Sixth "Day" he observed a contrasting fact—"God made the *beast of the earth*" (verse 24). The animals and their habitat are radically different in the two eras and yet expressed correctly and in their proper geological order. How any writer, no matter how early or late he appeared in the history of Babylonia, Phoenicia or Palestine, could have reconstructed all these accurate details out of the so-called chaotic Babylonian account of Creation, without divine suggestion, is extremely difficult for the average person to understand.

"After his kind" (Gen. 1: 25).

THE MIRACLE OF REPRODUCTION

The sacred writer, in introducing the new life of each era, has made a very definite statement in each case. This occurs in verses 11, 12, 21, 24 and 25 with almost stubborn regularity, and could not have been other than intentional. In the geological ages living things were created to produce "after their kind".

The fossil records, presented so well in the text-books on *geology and palaeontology, support this statement;* from the earliest Cambrian Period, when the waters had their jellyfish, sponges, and marine worms, right through the Palaeozoic and later eras to the life of our own times. There may be revealed varieties within any group, but never can be seen any variety of life mutating until it progresses into a new phylum.

Even in our modern times a horse mated with an ass will produce a mule, but mules are sterile and do not reproduce. A canary mated with a finch breeds a canary-mule, but canary-mules are sterile. A carp mated with a trout will not breed because we are told that they are not biological affinities. Apple blossom cannot be fertilised with pear pollen. Each particular type of flower or fruit must be fertilised with the pollen of its own particular group or biological affinity.

THE MIRACLE OF THE POLLEN

We do well to heed yet another authority upon this subject, but his viewpoint is from an altogether different angle. Here is what one of the foremost men of his generation had to say about the pollen of the flowers, and the miracle that each tremendously small, individual dusty speck of pollen is able to accomplish generation after generation:

"The stream of primordial protoplasm . . . has retained, even to the present, the fundamental characteristics that it had from the outset."

"That such is the case seems little less than a miracle; that an almost microscopical speck of protoplasm which we term a pollen grain, should contain the potentialities of thousands of generations of ancestors, and should be able to transmit them with such force that the seed growing from the ovule fertilized by that pollen grain will inevitably produce, let us say an apple tree, not a pear tree or a plum, is beyond comprehension. Yet we know it to be true."(103)

LIKE FATHER, LIKE SON

The miracle spoken of by Burbank in the pollen dust is repeated again in the passing on of the characteristics of parents to their children. Biological research has shown that the various parts of the body—for example, the skin, hair and eyes—have characteristics of colour, form and texture. These are represented in the body cells by little particles of matter called genes, which are scattered along rodlike carriers known as chromosomes. When the sperm fertilises the ovum in the reproductive cycle, there is a transference of these chromosomes to the offspring by either parent. One modern writer points out that in mankind there are forty-eight chromosomes in each adult cell, and the number of combinations of human characteristics possible gives the staggering total of almost 17 million.(104)

HOW DID GOD CREATE?

Geological research has shown that various groups of life arrived together in the same periods.

While the actual method of creation of different varieties within these groups of life may remain a mystery to us, yet does not our present understanding of some of the means of reproduction suggest that there could be no limit to the variety of new forms of life produced by the purposeful manipulation by an All-wise Creator of the chromosomes and genes of an original pair of any group.

PLANT RELATIONSHIPS

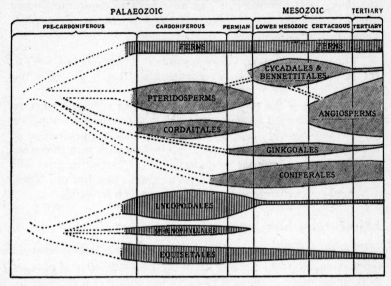

This interesting diagram appears in Prof. W. Howchin's publication, *The Building of Australia* (1938), p. 440. It is very interesting and important because it portrays the arrival and continuation or otherwise of the main groups of plants in the geological ages. The dotted lines shown by the author which connect the different groups of plants with each other are *entirely theoretical*. The palaeontologist thus reveals the fact that no fossil plants have been discovered that directly relate the groups (phyla) to each other. The beginnings of these plants according to this diagram are thus lost in the mist of evolutionary uncertainty.

Could we produce any better modern comment upon what the ancient writer recorded about 3,500 years ago when he said:

"And God made the beast of the earth *after his kind*, and cattle *after their kind*, and every thing that creepeth upon the earth *after his kind*"?

WHERE ARE THE MISSING LINKS?

Attention has already been drawn to the suddenness with which large groups of life appeared without apparent precursors.

1. At the beginning of the Palaeozoic: invertebrates.
2. During the Palaeozoic Era: vertebrates, insects.

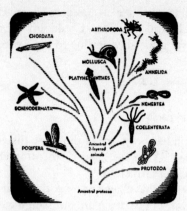

This diagram, which heads a paragraph titled " Invertebrate Relationships ", has been reproduced from the book *Animals without Backbones*, by
Ralph Buchsbaum (Penguin Series). It is a splendid illustration of the
statements made by this writer that "when we attempt to relate the phyla,
which by definition are groups of animals with fundamentally different
body plans, there is little we can say with certainty. . . . It is practically
no use relating the phyla to each other". In other words, the theory of
organic evolution cannot be demonstrated from the fossil evidence when
the relationships between the great groups of invertebrates (phyla) are
desired. Similar illustrations by writers dealing with other groups of
animals can be seen in *Science of Life*, p. 452, fig. 528; p. 499, fig. 572.

3. During the Devonian Period: terrestrial forest vegetation.
4. In the Mesozoic Era: great monsters of the sea and land,
   winged reptiles and birds.
5. In the Cretaceous Period: modern plants in great profusion,
   bees, and plant-fertilising insects.
6. In the Cainozoic and Quaternary Eras: animals of many
   varieties (mammals).

It is very suggestive, to say the least, that those who believe in
the theory of chance evolution are still searching, without success,
the geological strata, as they have for the past 100 years, for the
multitude of forerunners of the various types of life introduced so
suddenly. The Bible writer has not only been able to anticipate
the correct order of creation, corresponding to that given by
geologists, but has also placed certain types of life into groups and
described them accurately and picturesquely. Perhaps the
greatest fact to be noted is that, where the sacred record states
that God issued a creative command, or that another "day"
had been completed, it is usually at these positions represented
in the geological column that new types of life appear, and there

is a corresponding absence of precursors in the fossil record connecting the old and new life. Could any set of facts be more convincing and yet more devastating to any unsupported theory?

> **Day one, etc. (Gen. 1: 5).**

"Days" can be Eras

This translation has been one of the most-discussed passages of the creation story. Were the "days" mentioned of 24 hours, or were they special creative "days"?

In these studies we have been constantly reminded that originally the Bible was not written in our language. The Hebrew language, like many others, has words that have rather elastic meanings. In order to discover the meaning of a particular word we must carefully examine the context in which the word is used. If the context calls for merely daylight, or a "day" of 24 hours, then we must read it that way. If, however, the passage indicates a long period—prophetical, historical or otherwise—then we must translate the Hebrew word "yom" accordingly.

In this story of created things we have a record of developments that occurred on the earth from the period when it came into existence as a hot earth-mass, "without form and void", until it was thoroughly furnished with life and in the possession of those whom God had in view from the first. The passage indicates that all this was accomplished in *six "yoms"*.

Scientific Details Anticipated in Genesis

Referring to Tables A to F giving the chief features of the periods, and reading from the bottom of the columns, we find a number of items placed in the order accepted by sacred and scientific writers. When we examine the details of the groups supplied by the Scripture writers, we see that these extend to nearly fifty items. (Refer to summary at the rear of book, p. 153.)

Further, we notice that the One who inspired the record in the Book of Books also created the life that became fossilised and left its record in the Book of the Rocks, that men might read and interpret it. This has been done in the past 150 years, and those who will, see the one Great Creative Mind expressed in both records. But, while one record shows that the work occupied great periods of time, the Written Record, as given to us by the translators of 1611, refers to the periods as "days". The real question is, "Does the usage of the Hebrew word 'yom' allow for a longer period than 24 hours?" We find the answer in the Book of Books itself:

THE USE OF "YOM" IN GENESIS

1. In Genesis 1: 5, 14, 16, 18 *the period of light* is called "day". "God called the light, Day" (verse 5). In modern times we reverse this and speak of "daylight".
2. In Genesis 1: 14 the "day" *is* 24 *hours* (days and years).
3. In Genesis 2: 4 we see the much wider use of "yom": "These are the generations of the heavens and the earth when they were created in the 'day' that the Lord made the earth."

Here is our first suggestion of the unequalness of the time period, as given in the Hebrew word "yom". In summer, in Melbourne, Australia, the longest "day" has about 14 hours 47 minutes of light. In winter, the shortest "day" has about 11 hours 42 minutes of light. When we record the length of the "day" at the North or South pole we find that the "day" as defined in Genesis 1: 5, 14, 18 to be one of *six months*.

In the first chapter of Genesis the writer has given many details of the work done in *each of the six "days"*. Now in chapter 2 the writer compresses the six "days" creative work into one "day", which certainly suggests that "yom" has been used in this instance to specify a period other than merely daylight, or 24 hours.

THE "DAY" IN THE WILDERNESS

However, here are other references that can be checked by the reader, and which certainly call for a period *far beyond daylight, or 24 hours*:

4. Job 18: 20: "They that come after him shall be astonished at his 'day'."
5. Psalm 137: 7: "In the 'day' of Jerusalem."

6. Psalm 95:8: "'Day' of temptation in the wilderness."
7. Isaiah 11: 10–16: "In that 'day' . . . a root of Jesse."

See also Proverbs 16: 4; 21: 31; Isaiah 2: 11–12; 2: 17–20; 4: 1, 2; 10: 20.

Here are only a few of many references which could be used, but it will be seen that the word is frequently used *as a period of time*, and cannot always be confined to 24 hours.

"YOM" USED FOR A PERIOD

Let us further consider some of these references. The four quoted above will suffice for our purpose.

No. 4: The whole life-time of a man is compressed into a "yom" or "day" in much the same manner as modern people use the term.

No. 5: The "day" of Jerusalem, according to the context, no doubt refers to the period of 70 years when Jerusalem went into captivity in Babylon.

No. 6: The "day" here is defined by the context, verses 8–10, as one of "40 years", yet it is also referred to as "a day of temptation in the wilderness" for the Children of Israel, who had left Egypt led by Moses.

No. 7: Here is a reference to the "day" when the root of Jesse shall be glorious. Six verses are used to describe the events belonging to the work of the Lord in this "day" when He restores His people and blessing will come to other nations.

From these references we realise that the Hebrew word "yom" —translated "day"—can have a meaning which indicates: (1) unequal periods of daylight; (2) a 24-hour day; (3) a long period of time.

THE UNITY OF THE SCRIPTURES

However, there are several other thoughts that we should examine. In numerous discussions on this subject the Creation story of Genesis has been isolated from the presentations given in Job 38: 4–11; Proverbs 8: 22–29; Psalm 104: 5–9.

If we were to ask, When was the period in the earth's history mentioned in Proverbs 8: 24–29, when there were "no depths", "no mountains", "no hills", when He gave the sea His decree? or, referring to Job 38, when was the period when the foundations and cornerstone were developed? and when was it that the sea was born with clouds for garments?—as I have already endeavoured to portray, the scientists would answer, "All these things happened during the long period 'when the earth was without form and void', and before or about the period 'when darkness was upon the face of the deep'."

In other words, other Scripture passages which deal with the early history of the earth indicate what geologists and scientists have noted for us in the Book of the Rocks, that great periods of time were necessary, and that many geological ages can be bound up in the inspired words of Moses "the earth was without form and void" and "darkness was upon the face of the deep" and "the Spirit of God was continually brooding over the face of the waters".

Fossils Reveal Normal Development

Was God in a hurry? Another answer to this question is found in the evidence of the fossils. In the layers of the Cambrian period we find fossils of sponges, marine worms, starfish, jellyfish and shell-fish. The representatives of many of these creatures can be studied in the waters of the ocean today. There is nothing in the fossil evidence to indicate that life was hurried into unnatural development from eggs to adults who produced their young, etc., all within the range of a 24-hour day. The fossil evidence reveals normal development from eggs and young life to the adult stage, whether marine, terrestrial, vegetable or animal.

The Evidence of the Coal Beds

Again, we find layer upon layer of vegetation (as many as eighteen in one instance) represented in the coal beds. The fossils show that there was the growth from spore and seed in the usual way, and after maturity whole forests were submerged beneath the waters. Later, another forest grew, developed, and in time was submerged; and we have already observed that this process happened many times.

I

To imagine all these layers of growth developing one after another, from spore and seed to maturity, in the space of 24 hours, is to shut our eyes to facts and things observed in the vegetation developing around us today.

THE EVIDENCE OF THE MONSTERS

Fossil remains of dinosaur eggs were found in the Gobi desert and elsewhere, fossilised babies were found in the skeleton of a mother Ichthyosaurus. Surely the finding of these eggs and babies of the great monsters, mentioned as being created in the Fifth "Yom" or Period, convinces us that God allowed these creatures to develop along normal lines.

Finally, here is the opinion of a recognised Hebrew authority upon the subject:(106)

"The day, according to the scriptural reckoning of time, begins with the preceding evening."

"One day—not an ordinary day, but a day of God—an age. With Him a thousand years, nay, a thousand thousand years, are but as a day that is past. . . . The beginning of each period of creation is called 'morning'; its close 'evening', in the same way as we speak of the morning and evening of life."

> "There was evening, there was morning."

PLANNING AND ACCOMPLISHMENT

We have been looking together at the Scripture presentation of the work of the Great Architect upon this earth-mass. We have learned how He fashioned it, made secure its deep foundations, and then furnished it according to plans that He devised in the eternal ages (Matt. 25: 34).

We must keep in mind that this plan is only a portion of a yet greater master plan, of which we humans have at present only fragments of information revealed through the Scriptures.

We are, however, at present concerned with the first portion of the plan. This was carried out in a completely unhurried, leisurely way that becomes an Architect who has eternity in which to develop His purposes.

The Genesis story informs us that there were six stages, which had been translated "days", in which this portion of the plan was progressively developed. The details of each stage were carefully worked out. No earthly architect can proceed with the construction of the brickwork of a building until the concrete for the foundations has been poured and set. Again the floors must be laid, and the glass for the windows must be fitted, before the occupants can begin the process of supplying curtains and floor coverings and other furnishings.

The occupying of the building by the owners proceeds according to plans already made, and only when water and food have been made available.

The Amazing Architect Planned Creation

So it was with the Divine Architect. There was no one great spectacular command and then Hey presto!—the earth—its mountains, rivers, grasses, food, coal, continents and all the conveniences for mankind with domesticated animals, were completed. God never worked that way. The very picturesque language of the six stages of development has been examined, checked with information gleaned by independent scientific investigators and found to be delightfully correct.

We can better understand now what the sacred writer meant as he wrote his story. Each stage of development was planned by the Architect. In the east, the new day begins with the evening— the evening is the time for planning and discussion; with the light of the morning, the purposes of the evening are carried out in the order that will make for efficiency and stability. So, as the sacred writer anticipated each stage of the work planned in the evening and accomplished in the day, he made his record: "there was evening, there was morning—one 'era'," etc.

God Saw that It was Very Good

When the whole of the work was surveyed as a completed task the sacred writer was able to place on record:

"And God saw everything that He had made and, behold, it was very good. There was evening, there was morning, a Sixth Era."

There may be some who feel that such careful planning is not a becoming presentation of our All-wise Architect. Second thoughts, however, will, I am sure, lead such to see that it is indeed most becoming, and a viewpoint that has the authority of the Hebrew Scriptures.

For the last great act in the creation drama verse 26 gives this idea of planning first in the councils of God.

"And God said, *Let us make man* in our image, after our likeness: and let them have dominion over the fish of the sea, and over the fowl of the air, and over the cattle, and over all the earth."

Verse 27 notes the accomplishment of the plan:

"So God created man in his own image."

If we read the creation story again carefully we will notice that there are certain parts that seem to repeat. We can regard verse 6 as the formation of the plan and verse 7, its accomplishment. It is then that the thought of evening and morning, plan and action, is understood.

BIBLIOGRAPHY

103. *Plant Affinities*, vol. xi, p. 232, Luther Burbank. **104.** *Genetics and the Races of Man*, p. 46, Prof. W. C. Boyd, 1950. **106.** *The Pentateuch and Haftorahs*, Genesis, Chief Rabbi J. H. Hertz.

THE SIXTH ERA (*continued*):
MAN, GOD'S LIVING MASTERPIECE

The Sacred Record: Genesis 1: 26–28

"AND GOD SAID:

Let us make man in our image, after our likeness: and let them have dominion over the fish of the sea, and over the fowl of the air, and over the cattle, and over all the earth, and over every creeping thing that creepeth upon the earth.

So God created man in his own image, in the image of God created he him; male and female created he them.

And God blessed them, and God said unto them, Be fruitful and multiply, and replenish the earth and subdue it: and have dominion over the fish of the sea, and over the fowl of the air, and over every living thing that moveth upon the earth."

THE SIXTH ERA (*continued*):
MAN, GOD'S LIVING MASTERPIECE

> "And God said, Let us make man in our own image and after our likeness and let them have dominion . . ." (Gen. 1: 26).

Of All the Things Upon the Earth, Man is God's Masterpiece

He is the one being that can deliberately plan complex schemes, choose, search out, fashion materials, and become the conqueror of any adverse circumstances in which he may find himself.

The Scriptures, which in many details have supplied such an accurate account of the creation, have not by any means overstated the facts about man as he was created. We are informed that he was to have dominion over other things. We are also told that he was made in the image and likeness of his Creator.

Man, God's masterpiece, as he is seen today has become defiled, degraded and corrupted, and his will, affections, desires and thoughts have become perverse and alienated from his Creator.

But though the image of his Creator within him has become defiled and degraded, yet it is there, and man has always been able to keep in subjection the other creatures even from earliest times. He has so dominated the earth that he is the only animal capable of using its immense hidden and apparent resources in any profitable way.

Man Alone Exploits the Earth

He has searched the earth, its heights and hollows, and even its ocean depths, to discover food and materials for his own physical, economic or social needs. Man straddles the earth with steel rails and locomotives. He dominates the atmosphere with terrifying jet-propelled aircraft. His floating palaces, cargo boats and ships of war speed over and under the oceans.

All these utilities are the product of much experience, highly trained and specialised thinking on the part of his naval, military, and civil engineers, technicians and craftsmen. But more than this: behind all the specialists, there are the vast armies of miners and other workmen, who labour to extract oil, coal, minerals, timbers and other materials from their many hiding-places. After these we see vast multitudes of trained and untrained organised workers whose business it is to exploit these materials, and with very complicated machines and processes, when they so desire, force these to do their bidding, even to the thousandth part of an inch.

An evil-smelling and unintelligent bat may be equipped by its Maker with a splendid radar devise that will allow it, when blindfolded, to avoid the snares of an intelligent experimenter, but it cannot otherwise exploit its advantage. It took many years of thinking, planning, experiments, and hard work for intelligent men to discover the secret which had been held by this unintelligent and evil-smelling creature from its birth.

THE EARTH MADE FOR MAN

As man finds himself today, he is the only animal capable of using the earth and exploiting its multitudinous products to the best advantage. From our correlations of the creation story of Genesis with the geological material we seem to be forced to a very obvious conclusion, viz. that the Bible presentation is a divinely inspired one. The earth was made for man and man was fashioned to exploit the earth and its materials and creatures. Its resources, however, have been so placed and hidden that it has been a constant challenge to him, to discover, mine, and prepare them for his use.

No doubt this is just what his Creator intended. He wanted the matured physical, social, economic, political and international needs of mankind to challenge man, to him there would be the joy of discovery and the satisfaction of accomplishment.

However, behind all this there was his God's tremendous moral challenge. How would man, who had isolated himself from God, use these things? Would he selfishly possess them and make them to glorify himself in luxurious living? Would he use them to make war upon his fellows and his neighbours? There is nothing that so demonstrates man's spiritual depravity as when we see him at war with his fellows, and unable to avoid world-wide catastrophic consequences. God is thus demonstrating man's moral bankruptcy to himself. When he is faced with the possibility of a third world war with atomic power at his disposal and the possibility of men being destroyed by tens of thousands instead of ten in one moment, only then does he become really frightened at the consequences.

Confusion about Early Man

Great confusion of mind exists today because of the tremendous volume of literature that exists upon the subject of early man, and which is quite contrary to the letter and spirit of the Genesis record.

So far, we have been looking at a delightful array of correlations between the sacred and rock records, and observing that where it has been possible to test it, the sacred story is not proving to be scientifically inaccurate. Nor in the opinion of the writer is there any need for us to be in the least concerned about the truth or scientific accuracy of the rest of the story of Genesis relating to man's creation and his early history.

Here are a few pointers to the class of evidence which is now available:

(a) The Earliest Village Life in Asia

Quite recently, excavating on behalf of the Oriental Institute University of Chicago at a place called Jarmo, near Kirkuk in Mesopotamia, Professor R. Braidwood laid bare the remains of what he has been pleased to record as "The earliest village life of mankind in Asia".(107) In the layers he has uncovered the site of a very early village. All the details paraded by him are exactly those every student with faith in the Bible would expect.

The professor is able to tell us that agriculture was practised and that domestication of animals is recognisable from the bones of young sheep and goats. The site covers about three acres and has about eight levels. The upper levels contained sherds of early portable pottery, while the lower two-thirds were pre-ceramic levels in which flints and sickle-blades were abundant.(108) Needless to say, Jarmo is situated near the area of two of the rivers mentioned in the Bible "Eden" story. Almost a sensation has been created by the date (5270–4630 B.C.) arrived at by using the latest C 14 carbon method.(109)

This is not the place to go into the details concerning the popular conceptions which have been written about prehistoric life, because it is intended to deal with this subject in a later publication, but it should be mentioned here that the Bible has, in the writer's opinion, a complete answer to the chronological guesswork that has oftentimes been put out in the name of science.

(b) The Problem of Glacial Periods

Some points of confusion need to be mentioned because the average layman has little chance of dealing with them. The first one is the matter relating to glacial periods and early man, and the tremendous lengths of time ascribed to these. The data revealing that there was a glacial period, which particularly involved Northern Europe and North America, is unquestionable. What matters most is at what point in the period or periods did man first appear. If we allow that God placed man in Eden near the end of the last glacial period and God sent a flood upon the earth about 2,000 years later, then the facts about glacial times and early man could be interpreted more easily. When we come to think of it 2,000 years is a long period in man's history.

(c) The Problem of Palaeolithic Man

There is the further point with regard to Palaeolithic man. We must be reminded that the French people were the first to find and interpret Palaeolithic flints as being the tools of early man. It took quite a lot of talking by French research workers to convince our British grandfathers that these flints were actually the products of men. After years of patient work in this field of research a great assembly of various types of tools was gathered and systematised, but the important part of the story is that about this time the theory of the evolution of man became very popular. As this research work progressed, the French workers placed hundreds of thousands of years upon the age of these flints.

There are no dates stamped upon the flints, nor were these found in any context that would assist in giving any absolute dates to them. The finders of the flints, therefore, quite naturally interpreted the dating after their own ideas. It is true that they looked at certain levels in certain rivers in which the flints were discovered and calculated the levels in terms of the deposition of material as the rivers and/or glaciers normally deposit such material.

The Bible student, however, does not regard a flood which has left its evidence over various countries as being a normal slow means of depositing material. We surely have a right to assume that not only would such a universal cataclysm speed deposition in certain lakes and rivers, but it would also add some confusion to the surface layers and the position in the layers in which the flint evidence has been located.

(d) The Scripture Presentation

If we regard Palaeolithic man as being of the line of Cain, the hunter who went out from the presence of the Lord into the land of Nod (wandering) and lived about 2,000 years before the flood we have another answer to these material remains found in various lands. This is the viewpoint of Josephus, the Jewish historian,(111) as well as the interpretation of the Scripture story.

However, scientific men are searching for facts, and these facts are today causing research workers to think that "guess-work" dating of the past has been placed somewhat too early. (112)

Reconstructed Theories about Early Man

Let me give readers a sample of the reconstruction of thinking that is going on concerning early man and the theories that have been pronounced up to recently concerning certain skulls that have been recovered.

Dr. L. S. B. Leakey(113) has recently *written an article in which he points out* that "modern great apes were characterised by the presence of massive bony brow-ridges over the eyes and a ledge of bone on the inner aspect of the middle line of the jaw which is known as the Simian Shelf", and because some of the remains of early man in Europe and Asia had "massive brow-ridges" that "this came to be regarded as evidence of their primitive status", and incidentally paraded as "proof" of the evolutionary process.

Intensive research in Africa has now brought to light many fossil apes of early geological periods, and, "contrary to expectation, none of them have any signs of the Simian Shelf". Dr. Leakey, therefore, goes on to say that "We can, therefore, no longer regard the Simian Shelf as a primitive character . . . but we must regard it as being a highly specialised character of the jaw, which develops only in certain branches."

Fossil Apes Disprove a Theory

In other words, the scientists presumed previously that characteristics observed in modern great apes and early man, were signs of a family connection between the two. Now it has been discovered that the fossil evidence of others of the ape family does not acknowledge a family connection with humans, and so scientists have to reconstruct their theories.

The evidence of properly excavated sites is producing today much material that amply justifies the Bible description:

"And God created man in His own image, in the image of God created he him" (Gen. 1: 27).

Archaeological Evidence About the Flood

At a later date the writer expects to present evidence gathered from many modern authorities (glacial, geological and archeological) and demonstrate that the world-wide flood mentioned in Genesis cannot be easily brushed aside as being merely the exaggerated account of a local Mesopotamian incident. The facts gleaned by scientific men without any religious bias will be produced. These make a tremendously interesting, fascinating and thought-provoking story.

BIBLIOGRAPHY

107. *Sumer*, vol. vii, 1951, Prof. R. J. Braidwood. **108-9.** Jarmo. *Antiquity*, December 1950, Prof. R. J. Braidwood. **111.** Whiston's Josephus, *Antiquities*, Book 1, chap. 11, p. 103. **113.** *Science News*, No. 17, Penguin, Dr. L. S. Leakey.

EPILOGUE

We have been looking at a number of scientific facts concerning our earth which have been assembled by many recognised authorities from many countries over the past 150 years.

Some of the statements about the facts discovered by scientific men have been placed alongside other statements which have been presented in a very unique book, or really a library of books, and written by men who had a love for truth. It would not be out of place to again remind ourselves that the first record was written about 3,500 years ago, and the second perhaps 3,000 years ago.

We have seen that there is a very remarkable agreement between the facts searched out in modern times from the rocks and their layers, and the statements made by the sacred writers in ancient times. It seems almost unnecessary to say that the findings of the scientists have been made entirely independently of the statements made by the sacred writers. In fact, so misunderstood has been the sacred presentation that many scientists have ignored or ridiculed its record, but this fact only makes the challenge of the Bible presentation all the stronger.

There are, however, several very vital points of disagreement between certain statements of modern scientists and those of the sacred writers. Writers of text-books on biology, geology or palaeontology usually subscribe to the theory of chance evolution as being sufficient "cause" for things as we observe them today. In essence their claim and teaching is that out of chaos ultimately came the spectacular and orderly array of living things, until man himself arrived.

SACRED WRITERS REPUDIATE CHANCE

On the other hand, the sacred writers in presenting their viewpoints have made very definite statements which repudiate the chance element subscribed to by these men of science. The writer of the Book of Job has thrown out a tremendous challenge by his anticipation of some very illuminating details of certain events during the creation of the earth and the ocean. One can almost imagine him calling to all men—scientific, academic, business and otherwise, to all whatsoever—to note his most pertinent question:

"Where was thou when I laid the foundations of the earth?"

Well, where were we? I wonder—gas! water! hot mud! or what!!!

If this question leaves us searching mentally in something like the primeval fog we have been told about, this ancient writer asks yet another difficult question, and we certainly need the help of our modern astronomers to give us the data to understand it. So far as our present information goes, no other generation of men seems to have had the necessary knowledge to grasp the depth of meaning in it. It seems to have been written especially for our age and scientific men.

"Who determined the measurements?" (relative to the earth).

Who was it that selected our particular sun to be the father of our earth and family of planets? Why not one of the many super-suns we have told about? Again, who measured the distance and placed our sun just where it is, so that mankind and the life upon the earth are neither frozen nor burned, but receive the vital winter rains and summer heat for replenishing their annual food supplies?

The scientists have pointed out that the earth has a peculiar size. If it had been much larger problems would have been caused by continual masses being submerged by water, and atmospheric pressure being too great for living things as we know them. Chance can never work out an orderly system nor bring about the correlated design seen in creation.

If these very challenging questions have not yet convinced us that there was the One Great All-wise Creator superintending the vital measurements of the earth and its neighbours, one further question is presented to us. The questioner, however, this time not only asks the question but supplies us with certain very relevant and picturesque details of the incident. He seems to be perfectly informed about this creation business! Listen again to him:

"Who shut up the sea behind strong doors when it brake forth from the womb, when I made the cloud the garment thereof and thick darkness a swaddling band for it?"

The writer of this narrative has ruled out any element of chance as being the father of this creation. The context of these arresting questions shows that it is creation's Great Architect Himself who has asked them, and we notice how He has also supplied us with the information that anticipated the scientific explanations about the birth of the ocean. The anticipation of such very precise knowledge is never the child of chance or fortuitous guesswork.

Purposeful Creation

The Genesis writer also has ruled out this chance, purposeless element from his majestic and picturesque presentation of the earth's early eras. Just at that point where the geologists discover the first abundant demonstration of life in the Cambrian Period, which causes them to enquire about the beginnings and abundance of diversified life, the sacred writer has stated his case positively and picturesquely.

"The Spirit of God was [continually] brooding over the face of the waters."

Just here let us refer to a quotation from that compendium of information, *The Science of Life*, by Wells and Huxley. It is so very interesting to reproduce the author's own idea about the very fortuitous beginning of life.

"It is much more likely that at one moment in earth's cooling down, the warm seas provided an environment never afterwards to be repeated, an environment differing in temperature, in pressure in the salts within the waters, in the gases of the atmosphere over the waters, from any earlier or any later environments. The earth at that moment fulfilled all the conditions which the alchemists tried to repeat in the crucibles. It was a cosmic test tube whose particular brew led to the appearance of living matter as inevitably as an earlier

K

and different set of conditions led to the formation of rocks and seas and clouds" (p. 433).

ALL LIFE REPRODUCES AFTER ITS KIND

Now that is the best explanation that men of learning can offer us. Perhaps some of the thoughts expressed may contain some good ideas of what happened, but pure chance is substituted for purposeful creation. The sacred writer of Genesis, however, presses home his knowledge of his subject—he allows no compromise where "chance" has been substituted by men for Creative Wisdom. As this writer continues his record, which is a revelation of the orderly progress of the varied life that appeared, he repeatedly calls our attention to the fact that vegetation, monsters, flying things and mammals were created to reproduce offspring, so that similar life would continue. He makes a feature of the fact that each new type of life reproduced "after its kind". This is his claim, and it is exactly how we find life acting today. It has continued that way from Cambrian times right through the geological eras. Of course, the Architect planned that there should be different varieties of many of these living things, just as we see different types and races of men.

One very striking fact faces us. We have had presented to us by very ancient writers over forty well-assorted facts about the creation of the earth and its life. A few fortuitous guesses by the ancients might have been possible, but a correct orderly parade of many groups of closely associated details is altogether too much for us to allow to pass as shrewd guesses.

A COMPLICATED CREATION CANNOT COME BY CHANCE

Here is the final challenge. A wheel-barrow is a fairly simple mechanical implement. But no monkey or chimpanzee has yet produced such a simple product, and, if the zoologist is correct, these animals have had much more time than man to think out such a useful device if they so desired. But it took a being with intelligence to produce one. We may, however, go further. Paley long ago pointed out to us that a watch with its delicate mechanism took much patient experimenting of very intelligent men to bring it to the stage of perfection as he beheld, over 100 years ago. No sane human being would imagine it to be the child of blind purposeless chance. But modern specialisation can take us much further with our reasoning. As we look at the panel of one of our jet-propelled aeroplanes, with its multiplicity of gadgets, registering very vital information about pressures, speeds, heights, fuel consumption, wind resistance and what not, we realise what an exceedingly involved and complicated machine man has produced. We can therefore take it as axiomatic that the more complicated the machine the greater is the intelligence needed to produce it.

With his microscope man beholds a complicated bit of single-celled life called amoeba, or he may turn aside to inanimate things and be amazed at the delightful arrangement of electrons, protons and neutrons that constitute the world within an atom of metal. As he examines many metals he cannot but be struck by the fact of the orderliness of the arrangement of these atomic children. Every peculiar element having its own specified number of electrons, protons and neutrons.

With the telescope turned upon the countless systems of space, the scientist recognises a similar sort of arrangement—only, instead of whirling orderly atoms, he beholds whirling spheres in countless groups, all of which suggest to us that the Architect of the heavens and the Designer of the atom is the same.

REPRODUCTION OF LIVING THINGS A COMPLICATED PROCESS

When the biologist looks at the physical frame of a human being he is never too tired of telling us what an extraordinary piece of living machinery it is. He observes various cells of living material becoming associated, and a leg or lung or some other part of the body is formed. After much patient research the various parts of these living machines are now seen to be very cunningly controlled by many extraordinary things called glands. The size, shape and usefulness of any particular vital part is balanced delicately yet faithfully by these captains of various processes of the body.

But the functions of the various complicated parts of the human frame have become so commonplace that they are very largely taken for granted. These bodies are able to reproduce off-spring like unto the parents. The living mechanism in some unexplained way is able to fashion exceedingly small and complicated things that men call genes and chromosomes.

These extremely small units of living matter have been so delicately made that they carry within themselves the germ plasm that will faithfully and almost photographically reproduce the varied characteristics of several generations of forebears.

A COMPLICATED PROCESS DEMANDS SUPERIOR INTELLIGENCE

The human mind cannot follow nor explain all the very delicate, accurate and tremendously involved series of processes incurred in the reproduction of animal life, nor can we explain the mechanism by which an oak-tree or other living thing produces in its seed the material that provide an exact replica of itself. When the ancient writer recorded this apparently simple phrase "after their kind" he certainly provided us moderns with some extremely interesting food for reverent thought.

The Genesis story becomes a modern challenge to mankind. In the beginning God created the atoms, the heavens and the earth. Creation's Amazing Architect in the opening chapters of this ancient book has left mankind a testimony which has been amply supported by modern scientific investigation to demonstrate to those who will heed it that it is His truth and His revelation to men.

The Eternal Majesty

"Have ye not known? have ye not heard?

Hath it not been told you from the beginning?

Have ye not understood from the foundations of the earth?

It is he that sitteth upon the circle of the earth, and the inhabitants thereof are as grasshoppers.

That stretcheth out the heavens as a curtain, and spreadeth them out as a tent to dwell in . . .

To whom then will ye liken me, or shall I be equal? saith the Holy One.

Lift up your eyes on high, and behold who hath created these things.

That bringeth out their host by number:

He calleth them all by names,

By the greatness of his might, not one faileth for that he is strong in power.

Hast thou not known? hast thou not heard, that the everlasting God, the Lord, the Creator of the ends of the earth, fainteth not, neither is weary? there is no searching of his understanding."

Isaiah 40: 21, 22, 25, 26, 28.

THE BIBLICAL DETAILS AND ORDER OF CREATION
AND THE
DETAILS AND ORDER SUGGESTED BY SCIENTISTS

THE BIBLE	SCIENCE
First Day or Era	*The Pre-Cambrian Period*
Genesis 1: 1–2 Creation was the result of the planning of the Great Intelligence—God.	No parallel. But agreement in the fact that wonderful design is quite apparent.
(1) The earth had a beginning.	Agreement.
(2) The early earth was unformed and void (of life).	Agreement.
(3) Job 38: 4–11. Its measurements were vital and predetermined.	Its measurements are vital to life as we know it.
(4) Its foundations have been deeply sunk (fastened).	Agreement.
(5) Its cornerstone is vital.	A very dense central core.
(6) The sea was first shut up (within the earth mass).	Agreement generally.
(7) It burst forth (as vapours) out of nature's womb.	Agreement generally.
(8) Accompanied by clouds as its garment.	Agreement.
(9) Thick darkness blotting out the sun's light was wrapped around it as a swaddling band.	Agreement.
(10) The early ocean dominated the earth.	Agreement.
(11) It was restrained (from its proud position) by the later continental masses.	Agreement that the continental masses gradually developed.
(12) Genesis 1:2. The early ocean was a turbulent one (implied in the Hebrew).	No evidence.
(13) After the early period of darkness, light came.	Agreement.
(14) The presence of the sun gave light.	Agreement.

THE BIBLE	SCIENCE
(15) There was a division between the light and between the darkness (day and night).	Agreement.
(16) Life came first to the waters of the ocean.	Agreement.
(17) The Spirit of God was the Creator of all life (the designer, selector and manipulator of chromosomes and genes).	Science is silent (but agrees that living things seem to be perfectly made and adapted to circumstances).
(18) The brooding of God's Spirit upon the waters of the ocean was continuous even from the period of so-called chaos (a term used by theologians).	Agreement that marvellous order somehow came out of what appeared to be primeval chaos.
Second Day or Era (19) The atmosphere was established.	Agreement; but science cannot explain how its perfect adjustment took place.
(20) The atmosphere divided ocean waters from atmospheric waters.	Agreement.
Third Day or Era (21) The dry land appeared out of the waters.	*Pre-Cambrian to Silurian* Agreement.
(22) The waters collected together into seas.	Agreement.
(23) Terrestrial vegetation appeared.	Agreement.
(24) This vegetation was of different kinds. Sproutage, naked seeds, and covered seeds.	Agreement.
(25) The vegetation reproduced after its kind.	The evidence of the fossils does not deny this.
Fourth Day or Era (26) The sun and moon now received new appointments from the Creator.	*Permian to Triassic Periods* Science is silent (but great climatic changes have been noted).
(27) They dominated the atmosphere after a period when they did *not* dominate.	Agreement that in places dry, desert conditions followed a period of inland seas and swamps.
28) Permanent seasons established.	Agreement. Seasons appear from this era as a permanent feature.
Fifth Day or Era (29) New types of life came to the *waters of the earth*.	*Mesozoic Era* Agreement.
(30) The waters swarmed with this new life.	Agreement.

THE BIBLE	SCIENCE
(31) Great monsters (reptilian) appeared on sea and land.	Agreement.
(32) Some of the species " glided swiftly " through the waters.	Agreement.
(33) Flying things arrived.	Agreement.
(34) These flying things reproduced after their kind.	The evidence of fossils does not deny this.
Sixth Day or Era (35) New types of life appeared *upon the land* (mammals).	*Cainozoic Era* Agreement.
(36) These consisted of beasts of the earth.	Agreement.
(37) And cattle.	Agreement.
(38) And creeping things.	Agreement.
(39) These reproduced after their kind.	The evidence of fossils does not deny this.
(40) Mankind appeared after the beasts and cattle (mammals).	Agreement.
(41) Man was the last of the creation.	Agreement.
(42) Man was made in the image of his Creator (free to will, choose, etc.).	Science is silent, but agrees that man is different from the apes.
(43) Man was given dominion over the animals of creation.	Man dominates the other animals.
(44) Man at first lived on the fruits of the earth.	General agreement.
(45) Man's special work was to replenish the earth and subdue it.	General agreement only.
(46) When God surveyed His finished work He pronounced it " Very good ".	Science offers no opinion except that it says that evolution somehow did a wonderful job out of an original hot earth-mass all by fortuitous chance.

APPENDIX A

There is a theory current among certain Christian teachers that in the beginning (Gen. i. 1) when God created the world, with His Almighty power and wisdom, such a creation was produced out of nothing, and that it was instantly brought into existence, perfect and complete.

The thought is then enlarged to convey the idea that judgment came to this original creation; then, as the result of such a judgment, the world "became waste and void" and darkness prevailed over the deep. In this condition it is suggested it remained for ages. We cannot, just here, deal exhaustively with this interpretation, but we will look at a few of the words and ideas used in the narratives to see whether this thought of suddenness in the creative process is acceptable or justified in the light of the usage of certain words not only throughout this narrative but also in other Scriptures.

Two words, both signifying action, stand out particularly— the first has been translated "create" (Hebrew—BARA), and the second has been rendered "formed" (Hebrew—YATSAR). We will first of all consult two authorities upon these words, authorities which are generally accepted in Christian circles.

Robert Young, LL.D. (*Analytical Concordance to the Bible*), gives us the following: "BARA, to form, fashion, create. Translated into the Greek—to make, produce, a thing made."

Jas. Strong, LL.D. (*Exhaustive Concordance of the Bible*), says: "BARA, a primitive root (absolute) create (qualified) to cut down (a wood) select, feed (as formative processes) choose, create, creator, cut down, dispatch, do, make (fat)."

We can see from the usages of the word BARA that a great number of ideas are involved in the meaning of this Hebrew word.

The second word YATSAR is translated as "formed", and both Strong and Young give us the idea of fashioning, forming, framing, making and also determining.

We can now examine these words in their contexts.

Genesis 2: 7. The Lord God *formed* (YATSAR) man out of the dust of the ground.

Genesis 2: 8. The Lord God planted a garden . . . there he put the man whom he had *formed*.

Of the coming of *woman*, however, a new idea is introduced.

Genesis 2: 22. The Lord God . . . took one of his ribs . . . made (builded) he a woman.

Here are specific statements giving details, though the processes employed are vague. Man was "formed" out of the dust of the ground. The woman was "builded" out of the rib of man.

We will now turn to the other specific statements about the man and the woman.

Genesis 1: 27. God "created" man in His own image . . . male and female "created" He them.

Genesis 5: 1. This statement is repeated, that man—"male and female"—was "created".

It seems then, from references noted, that the "creative" process was by "forming" and by "building" out of previously created material. Now a most interesting fact comes to light. The Hebrew word YATSAR translated "formed" is also translated "potter", so that the writer would imply that in some such way as a potter forms, fashions or manufactures a useful article with his hands out of the clay, so the Lord God, in some inscrutable way impossible for humans to understand, fashioned a man "out of the dust of the ground". Then from a part of the man the All Wise God "builded" a woman.

It would seem from these preliminary references that the words "create", "form" or "made" are interchangeable. God created man, or formed man out of the dust. God created woman, or builded her out of man.

If this interchangeability is correct, then we would expect to find the idea used in other parts of the Scriptures. This is indeed what we discover.

In Isaiah 43: 1—"Thus saith the Lord that 'CREATED' thee, O Jacob, and 'FORMED' thee, O Israel."

In Isaiah 43: 15—"I am the Lord your Holy One, the 'CREATOR' of Israel."

The children of Ammon are spoken of: "In the place where thou wast 'created' will I judge thee" (Ezek. 21: 30).

Jacob is spoken of as being "created"—something that did not happen suddenly, nor yet without human means. In much the same way, the children of Ammon are "created" in their land. The Holy One is spoken of as being the "creator" of Israel—43: 15—and yet in 43: 1 Israel as having been "formed" by the Lord. Also note the following:

Amos 4: 13. He that "FORMETH" the mountains and "CREATETH" the wind.

Isaiah 45: 7. He "FORMS" the light and "CREATES" darkness.

Genesis 2: 19. The Lord God "FORMED" every beast of the field and every fowl of the air.

Genesis 1: 21. God "CREATED" great monsters and every living thing that moveth after their kinds and every winged fowl after his kind.

From these references, which can be multiplied, we see that the vital words "create" and "form" have been used interchangeably, both by the Genesis and other later Hebrew writers. The same thing applies to the idea of creation. It is not something brought into being suddenly—perfectly and completely. God can, if He so will, do all of these things in the way suggested, but the usage of these words by the Hebrew writers shows us that, in the passages indicated, this sudden and complete perfection was evidently not intended.

In this discussion the writer does not subscribe to the theory of the eternity of matter. God brought into existence the material from which He "formed", "fashioned" or "created" the heavens and the earth. This principle is seen also in the development of the Christian. The believer, from very imperfect material, is accepted as a "new creation in Christ". He is by no means suddenly perfected and complete, but as a yielded pliable individual he is fashioned by the Holy Spirit of God in the everyday experiences of life, until ultimately he stands in the presence of God, perfected and "fashioned anew" (Phil. 3: 20–21 R.V.).

THE AUSTRALIAN INSTITUTE OF ARCHAEOLOGY

The Institute's Aims and Objects

The Australian Institute of Archaeology was formally constituted in September 1946. Its chief objectives, as set out in its articles, are stated to be:

"To investigate, search and publicise, by means of scientific methods, all discoveries, findings and results which the Institute, or any person, University, Museum or other organisation, shall publish calculated to have a bearing upon the authenticity, historicity, accuracy and inspiration of the Holy Scriptures."

In view of the vast amount of relevant material which bears on the Scriptures, and which has come to light during the past 50 years, this Institute feels a responsibility not only to the Christian Church but also to the general public to make known these facts which will contribute much towards commending to our modern society the trustworthiness of Holy Scriptures, that bulwark of national life.

Members of Council

President: W. J. Beasley, F.R.G.S.
Vice-Presidents: Rev. L. L. Morris, B.Sc., M.Th., Ph.D.
Rev. H. M. Arrowsmith, Th.L.
Director: J. A. Thompson, M.Sc., B.A., B.Ed. B.D.
Secretary and Treasurer: R. C. Wilkins, B.Com.
Executive Committee: W. J. Beasley,   G. J. Charlton,
W. M. Pollard,   R. C. Wilkins.
Members of Council: F. I. Andersen, M.Sc.
G. J. Charlton, L.L.B.
A. M. Clarke, F.R.C.S.
Rev. W. R. McEwan, B.A.
W. M. Pollard, F.C.I.S., F.F.I.A.
Rev. J. W. Searle, B.A., B.D.
Paul H. H. White, M.B., B.S.

Exhibition: Ancient Times House, 116 Little Bourke St., Melbourne.

The Institute is registered as a non-profit-sharing company and seeks to extend its usefulness as funds are available.
Australian Offices: 174 Collins St., Melbourne, C.1.

The Creation Story a...

GEOLOGICAL PERIODS
placed in ideal order

GEOLOGICAL ERAS

CHIEF BIOLOGICAL AND GEOL...
as noted by fossil remains found in t...

GEOLOGICAL PERIODS	GEOLOGICAL ERAS
RECENT OR HOLOCENE ⑯	QUATERNARY
PLEISTOCENE ⑯ ⑮	
PLIOCENE	TERTIARY or CAINOZOIC
MIOCENE	
OLIGOCENE ⑭	
EOCENE	
CRETACEOUS ⑬	SECONDARY or MESOZOIC
JURASSIC ⑩ ⑪ ⑫	
TRIASSIC	
PERMIAN ⑩	
⑧ ⑨ CARBONIFEROUS	
DEVONIAN ⑥ ⑧	PRIMARY or PALAEOZOIC
⑥ SILURIAN ⑦ ⑨	
ORDOVICIAN	
CAMBRIAN ⑤ ④	
PROTEROZOIC ④ ⑤	
ARCHAEOZOIC ④? ③ ②	ARCHAEAN

READ UPWARDS

ERA OF MAN
The Intelligent Creature that ⑯
can will and choose — the one
creature who dominates all
other creatures. ⑮

3%

ERA OF MAMMALS (modern)
⑭ Wild Beasts and Cattle
Mesozoic Life dies out

7%

ERA OF GIGANTIC REPTILES ⑫
Winged Lizards, Birds, Etc. ⑪
Trees with well-developed annual ri...
New Saurian Life ⑩c
Mesozoic Life appears

Great Climatic changes noted ⑩b Pala...
Alternation of Glacial and Temperate
Stupendous changes in Earth's c...
Coal Beds in Australia   Desert

17%

⑨ ERA OF VEGETATION AND T...
Luxuriant Vegetation & Cloudy Carbon...
VARVES in shales indicating seasonal ⑩a c...
Seed bearing Plants in Profusion.
Trees with covered seeds (fruit).   Co...

Amphibia (water and land air breathing
Fish —   life with vertebrae.
Insects (Air breathing) ⑥a
Land made Equable for vegetation a...

ERA OF INVERTEBRATES (mar...
Marine Life in abundance and highl...
diversified — Trilobites with compou...
Sponges — Worms — Graptolites — Moll...
Echinoderms — Brachiopods — Etc.
Approximately 455 Species now iden...

73%

Fossils rare   Marin...

No FOSSILS OF TERRESTR...

Glacial Period

No known fossils ❶
Immense Quantities of Vapour E...
Raining continually — Dark
Water covering the face of the Glo...

Check the parallels num...
the column on the right with the cent...

ESTIMATED PERCENTAGE OF GEOLOGICAL TIME

AUSTRALIAN INSTITUTE OF A...